Vocabulary
Power Plus for
College and Career Readiness

LEVEL
NINE

By Daniel A. Reed
Edited by Paul Moliken

Prestwick House

P.O. Box 658 • Clayton, DE 19938
(800) 932-4593 • www.prestwickhouse.com

Prestwick House, Inc.
P.O. Box 658 • Clayton, DE 19938
(800) 932-4593 • www.prestwickhouse.com

Vocabulary
Power Plus for
College and Career Readiness

•Table of Contents•

Vocabulary Power Plus for College and Career Readiness

LEVEL
NINE

·Introduction·

VOCABULARY POWER PLUS FOR COLLEGE AND CAREER READINESS combines classroom-tested vocabulary drills with reading and writing exercises designed to foster the English and language arts skills essential for college and career success, with the added advantage of successfully preparing students for both the Scholastic Assessment Test and the American College Testing assessment.

Although *Vocabulary Power Plus* is a proven resource for college-bound students, it is guaranteed to increase vocabulary, improve grammar, enhance writing, and boost critical reading skills for students at all levels of learning.

Critical Reading exercises include lengthy passages and detailed, evidence-based, two-part questions designed to promote understanding and eliminate multiple-choice guessing. We include SAT- and ACT-style grammar and writing exercises and have placed the vocabulary words in non-alphabetical sequence, distributed by part-of-speech.

Coupled with words-in-context exercises, inferences cultivate comprehensive word discernment by prompting students to create contexts for words, instead of simply memorizing definitions. Related words-in-context exercises forge connections among words, ensuring retention for both knowledge and fluency, and nuance exercises instill active inference habits to discern not just adequate words for contexts, but the best words in a specific context.

The writing exercises in *Vocabulary Power Plus* are process-oriented and adaptable to individual classroom lesson plans. Our rubrics combine the fundamentals of the essay-scoring criteria for both the SAT and ACT optional writing portions, with emphasis on organization, development, sentence formation, and word choice. This objective scoring opportunity helps students develop a concrete understanding of the writing process and develop a personal approach to punctual, reactive writing.

We hope that you find the *Vocabulary Power Plus for College and Career Readiness* series to be an effective tool for teaching new words, and an exceptional tool for preparing for assessments.

Strategies for Completing Activities

Roots, Prefixes, and Suffixes

A knowledge of roots, prefixes, and suffixes can give readers the ability to view unfamiliar words as mere puzzles that require only a few simple steps to solve. For the person interested in the history of words, this knowledge provides the ability to track word origin and evolution. For those who seek to improve vocabulary, the knowledge creates a sure and lifelong method; however, there are two points to remember:

1. Some words have evolved through usage, so present definitions might differ from what you infer through an examination of the roots and prefixes. The word *abstruse*, for example, contains the prefix *ab–* (away) and the root *trudere* (to thrust), and literally means "to thrust away." Today, *abstruse* is used to describe something that is hard to understand.

2. Certain roots do not apply to all words that use the same form. If you know that the root *vin* means "to conquer," then you would be correct in concluding that the word *invincible* means "incapable of being conquered"; however, if you tried to apply the same root meaning to *vindicate* or *vindictive*, you would be incorrect. When analyzing unfamiliar words, check for other possible roots if your inferred meaning does not fit the context.

Despite these considerations, a knowledge of roots and prefixes is one of the best ways to build a powerful vocabulary.

Critical Reading

Reading questions generally fall into several categories.

1. Identifying the main idea or the author's purpose. *What is this selection about?*

In some passages, the author's purpose will be easy to identify because the one or two ideas leap from the text; however, other passages might not be so easily analyzed, especially if they include convoluted sentences. Inverted sentences (subject at the end of the sentence) and elliptical sentences (words missing) will also increase the difficulty of the passages, but all these obstacles can be overcome if readers take one sentence at a time and recast it in their own words. Consider the following sentence:

> These writers either jot down their thoughts bit by bit, in short, ambiguous, and paradoxical sentences, which apparently mean much more than they say—of this kind of writing Schelling's treatises on natural philosophy are a splendid instance; or else they hold forth with a deluge of words and the most intolerable diffusiveness, as though no end of fuss were necessary to make the reader understand the deep meaning of their sentences, whereas it is some quite simple if not actually trivial idea, examples of which may be found in plenty in the popular works of Fichte, and the philosophical manuals of a hundred other miserable dunces.

If we edit out some of the words, the main point of this sentence is obvious.

> These writers either jot down their thoughts bit by bit, in short ambiguous, and paradoxical sentences, which apparently mean much more than they say—of this kind of writing Schelling's treatises on natural philosophy are a splendid instance: or else they hold forth with a deluge of words and the most intolerable diffusiveness, as though [it] end of fuss were necessary to make the reader understand the deep meaning of their sentences, whereas it is some [a] quite simple if not actually trivial idea, examples of which may be found in plenty in the popular works of Fichte, and the philosophical manuals of a hundred other miserable dunces.

Some sentences need only a few deletions for clarification, but others require major recasting and additions; they must be read carefully and put into the reader's own words.

> Some in their discourse desire rather commendation of wit, in being able to hold all arguments, than of judgment, in discerning what is true; as if it were a praise to know what might be said, and not what should be thought.

After studying it, a reader might recast the sentence as follows:

> In conversation, some people desire praise for their abilities to maintain the conversation rather than their abilities to identify what is true or false, as though it were better to sound good than to know what is truth or fiction.

2. Identifying the stated or implied meaning. *What is the author stating or suggesting?*

The literal meaning of a text does not always correspond with the intended meaning. To understand a passage fully, readers must determine which meaning—if there is more than one—is the intended meaning of the passage. Consider the following sentence:

> If his notice was sought, an expression of courtesy and interest gleamed out upon his features; proving that there was light within him and that it was only the outward medium of the intellectual lamp that obstructed the rays in their passage.

Interpreted literally, this Nathaniel Hawthorne metaphor suggests that a light-generating lamp exists inside the human body. Since this is impossible, the reader must look to the metaphoric meaning of the passage to understand it properly. In the metaphor, Hawthorne refers to the human mind—consciousness—as a lamp that emits light, and other people cannot always see the lamp because the outside "medium"—the human body—sometimes blocks it.

3. Identifying the tone or mood of the selection. *What feeling does the text evoke?*

To answer these types of questions, readers must look closely at individual words and their connotations; for example, the words *stubborn* and *firm* have almost the same definition, but a writer who describes a character as *stubborn* rather than *firm* is probably suggesting something negative about the character.

Vocabulary Power Plus for College and Career Readiness includes evidence-based follow-up questions in every critical reading lesson, as prescribed by the Partnership for Assessment of Readiness for College and Careers (PARCC) consortium, and will be used in the 2016 revision of the SAT. These questions prompt for the contextual evidence that students use to answer the primary questions.

Writing

The optional writing portions on the two major assessment tests allow approximately 30 minutes for the composition of a well-organized, fully developed essay. Writing a satisfactory essay in this limited time requires facility in determining a thesis, organizing ideas, and producing adequate examples to support the ideas.

These fundamentals are equally important for success on the Smarter Balanced Assessment Consortium ELA Performance Task, which includes a substantial essay writing assignment based on provided source texts.

Such a time-limited essay might lack the perfection and depth that weeks of proofreading and editing provide research papers. Process is undoubtedly of primary importance, but students must consider the time constraints of both reality and those of the assessments they elect to complete. Completion of the essay is just as important as organization, development, and language use.

The thesis, the organization of ideas, and the support make the framework of a good essay. Before the actual writing begins, writers must create a mental outline by establishing a thesis, or main idea, and one or more specific supporting ideas (the number of ideas will depend on the length and content of the essay). Supporting ideas should not be overcomplicated; they are simply ideas that justify or explain the thesis. The writer must introduce and explain each supporting idea, and the resultant supporting paragraph should answer the *Why?* or *Who cares?* questions that the thesis may evoke.

Once the thesis and supporting ideas are identified, writers must determine the order in which the ideas will appear in the essay. A good introduction usually explains the thesis and briefly introduces the supporting ideas. Explanation of the supporting ideas should follow, with each idea in its own paragraph. The final paragraph, the conclusion, usually restates the thesis or summarizes the main ideas of the essay.

Adhering to the mental outline when the writing begins will help the writer organize and develop the essay. Using the Organization and Development scoring guides to evaluate practice essays will help to reinforce the process skills. The Word Choice and Sentence Formation scoring guides will help to strengthen language skills—the vital counterpart to essay organization and development.

Vocabulary Power Plus for College and Career Readiness includes two styles of writing prompts. SAT-style writing prompts feature general subjects such as art, history, literature, or politics. ACT-style writing prompts involve subjects specifically relevant to high school students. Both styles of writing prompts require students to assume a point of view and support it with examples and reasoning.

Pronunciation Guide

a	—	track
ā	—	mate
ä	—	father
â	—	care
e	—	pet
ē	—	be
i	—	bit
ī	—	bite
o	—	job
ō	—	wrote
ô	—	port, **fought**
ōō	—	proof
ŏŏ	—	full
u	—	pun
ū	—	**you**
û	—	purr
ə	—	about, system, su**pp**er, circ**u**s
oi	—	toy
îr	—	steer

Word List

Lesson 1
alienate
cogitate
elated
epigram
fatalistic
gall
lackadaisical
licentious
numismatist
obtrude
parry
paucity
pensive
ruffian
transpire

Lesson 2
amalgamate
antiquated
beleaguer
broach
caricature
dally
demented
enshroud
felonious
gorge
hone
opiate
prose
renaissance
surcharge

Lesson 3
ambidextrous
animate
belated
berserk
chauvinist
deliberate
delude
edifice
egalitarian
forum
insurrection
knead
maul
ostentatious
thesis

Lesson 4
accentuate
blight
composite
denizen
elude
entice
fallow
fealty
fruition
gambit
gratify
laggard
navigable
obsequy
transcribe

Lesson 5
advocate
bandy
charisma
dastardly
efface
entity
ingrate
intervene
gist
jaded
jeopardize
mesmerize
ogre
status quo
waylay

Lesson 6
begrudge
bibliophile
cadence
commandeer
declaim
enmity
gaffe
glutinous
imbue
indisposed
mandarin
nepotism
quaff
sally
stark

Word List

Lesson 7
cadaverous
daunt
despot
dote
egress
exuberance
flux
gird
gothic
hovel
laminate
penury
primeval
substantiate
tenure

Lesson 8
allude
beget
chafe
desist
educe
effrontery
elite
feign
gaunt
glean
guerilla
imbibe
mire
sector
undue

Lesson 9
aghast
bilk
choleric
decadence
demise
emit
eradicate
fabricate
ghastly
granary
homily
impede
lampoon
narcissistic
qualm

Lesson 10
affiliate
bane
berate
blatant
calumny
dawdle
desolate
fallible
fawn
filch
garble
minion
neophyte
pacify
prevaricate

Lesson 11
carp
emissary
façade
flagrant
fracas
futile
gait
genesis
immaculate
kindred
lacerate
nefarious
patrician
query
queue

Lesson 12
anthropomorphic
aplomb
beneficiary
careen
catholic
deluge
eerie
fester
guile
havoc
languish
martial
modicum
pall
rancid

Word List

Lesson 13
anachronism
defunct
denigrate
effusive
embroil
envisage
gape
holocaust
humane
impertinent
lackey
lament
lethal
lofty
nemesis

Lesson 14
alacrity
benediction
carnage
catalyst
deify
epitaph
foible
frivolous
harp
impel
impetuous
jargon
judicious
lateral
pallid

Lesson 15
adjunct
chicanery
debonair
deplete
equivocal
farcical
feisty
filial
genealogy
gull
impervious
macabre
mitigate
nadir
penchant

Lesson 16
admonish
affliction
aphorism
cache
daub
delete
impermeable
lax
mendicant
obeisance
oscillate
oust
paean
palpable
smug

Lesson 17
aloof
bias
cavort
desecrate
ensue
fiat
fidelity
fluent
gyrate
hilarity
melee
pariah
pedagogue
personification
rambunctious

Lesson 18
allocate
belabor
conjecture
faux
foray
genocide
gratis
manifesto
materialistic
monolithic
predilection
progeny
quintessential
resign
rudimentary

Word List

Lesson 19
amenable
conducive
influx
junta
mollify
patina
perjury
pinnacle
placebo
plaintive
rigorous
sedentary
stricture
subversive
tantamount

Lesson 20
acumen
concurrent
crony
erroneous
impasse
insular
irrevocable
malodorous
nanotechnology
negligible
notarize
precept
pungent
renege
visage

Lesson 21
botch
brinkmanship
confute
dynasty
forte
fortitude
ineffable
kleptomania
meritorious
mezzanine
perennial
purport
recumbent
renown
tribulation

Lesson One

1. **gall**   (gôl)   *n.*   shameless boldness; nerve
    The thief had the *gall* to sue the store owner because the guard dog had bitten him while he robbed the cash register.
    syn: insolence; impudence   *ant: shyness; modesty*

2. **parry**   (par´ ē)   *v.*   to deflect or evade a blow, especially in swordfighting
    The castle defender *parried* the invader's battle axe and delivered a fatal lunge with his sword.
    syn: repel

3. **cogitate**   (ka´ jə tāt)   *v.*   to think deeply
    Allen *cogitates* while he mows the hayfield, figuring out how he will keep the farm operating for yet another year.
    syn: ponder; ruminate

4. **transpire**   (tran spī´ ər)   *v.*   to happen; to take place
    Detective Murphy looked at clues from the crime scene and guessed what had *transpired* there on the night of the murder.
    syn: occur   They looked at the mess and started 2 remembered what had transpired.

5. **ruffian**   (ru´ fē ən)   *n.*   a brutal, lawless person
    After they shot up the general store and harassed the locals, the *ruffians* were captured by the sheriff and thrown into jail.
    syn: thug; bully   The ruffian robbed the store.

6. **licentious**   (lī sen´ shəs)   *adj.*   morally unrestrained
    Like St. Augustine, some people want to abandon their *licentious* lifestyles, but not immediately.
    syn: immoral; lewd   *ant: chaste; pure*

7. **numismatist**   (nōō miz´ mə tist, mis´)   *n.*   a coin collector
    My father is a *numismatist* who has hundreds of coins from ancient Rome.
    My grandad is a numismatist & has 100s of coins.

8. **paucity**   (pô´ si tē)   *n.*   a scarcity; a lack
    The *paucity* of jobs in the small town forced Jack to find work elsewhere.
    syn: insufficiency   *ant: abundance*

9. **fatalistic** (fā təl is´ tik) *adj.*   believing that all events in life are inevitable
and determined by fate
Fatalistic thinkers believe there is nothing they can do to change the course of their
lives.

10. **obtrude** (ob trōōd´) *v.*   to force oneself into a situation uninvited
You were concentrating on your work, so I did not wish to *obtrude*.
syn: impose; intrude She   obtruded *ant: extricate* the boys
yonw party).

11. **pensive** (pen´ siv) *adj.*   dreamily thoughtful
Jane was in a *pensive* mood after she finished reading the thought-provoking novel.
syn: reflective; meditative   *ant: silly; frivolous*

12. **lackadaisical** (lak ə dāz´ i kəl) *adj.*   uninterested; listless
The *lackadaisical* student sat in the detention hall and stared out the window.
syn: spiritless; apathetic; languid   *ant: enthusiastic; inspired*

13. **alienate** (âl ē i nāt) *v.*   to turn away feelings or affections
Your sarcastic remarks might *alienate* your friends and family.
syn: estrange   *ant: endear; unite*

14. **elated** (i lā´ tid) *adj.*   in high spirits; exultantly proud and joyful
We were *elated* to learn that our team would move on to finals.   a   car 4
syn: overjoyed She was   *ant: depressed*   her b-day.
elated when she   got

15. **epigram** (e´ pi gram) *n.*   a witty saying expressing a single thought
or observation
The author placed relevant *epigrams* at the beginning of each chapter.
syn: aphorism; bon mot; quip

Exercise I

Words in Context

From the list below, supply the words needed to complete the paragraph. Some words will not be used.

isolate ~~alienate~~ epigram ~~fatalistic~~ ~~lackadaisical~~
~~licentious~~ obtrude ~~paucity~~

1. Byron's _obtrude_ notion that he possessed no control over his decisions eventually became his excuse for living a[n] _licentious_ lifestyle. He partied nightly, and his _paucity_ of ambition or goals had _alienate_ him from his relatively successful friends. When they tried to talk to Byron about his future, his only response was a[n] _lackadaisical_ stare.

From the list below, supply the words needed to complete the paragraph. Some words will not be used.

~~elated~~ ~~obtrude~~ alienate ~~numismatist~~
parry pensive ~~epigram~~ paucity - lack

2. Jenny, who lives by Ben Franklin's _epigram_, "Early to bed and early to rise, makes a man healthy, wealthy, and wise," arrived at the flea market at six a.m. It took her two hours to find what she was looking for—a pre-Revolutionary-era silver dollar. A[n] _pensive_ elderly woman sat behind the stand in the shade of a canvas tarp, reading a leather-bound novel.
   "I'm sorry to _obtrude_," said Jenny, "but what are you asking for this old coin?" The old woman looked up from her book, smiled, and said, "Make me an offer." As an experienced _numismatist_, Jenny knew the exact value of the coin. She offered half, and Jenny was _elated_ when the woman accepted her offer, without even having to _parry_ endlessly with her on the price.

From the list below, supply the words needed to complete the paragraph. Some words will not be used.

gall ~~ruffian~~ ~~cogitate~~ fatalistic
parry ~~transpire~~ pensive

3. When a statue of the town's founder was found knocked over, police attributed the vandalism to a group of _ruffian_ roaming the neighborhood; however, after Inspector Courson _cogitates_ for a few minutes while looking at the crime scene, she was able to disprove the officers' theory as to how the event _transpired_. Only one person in town would have the _gall_ to damage the statue of the beloved founder, and the inspector knew why.

Exercise II

Sentence Completion

Complete the sentence in a way that shows you understand the meaning of the italicized vocabulary word.

1. You might *alienate* your friends if you…
   sit at a different table as them.

2. The traffic jam on the interstate *transpired* after…
   the car accident

3. If you were not invited to the party, then don't *obtrude* by…
   going to the party.

4. Few people have enough *gall* to…
   yell at a teacher.

5. The *lackadaisical* player was cut from the team because…
   he didn't want to be there

6. Someone who suffers a *paucity* of willpower might find it difficult to…
   lose weight

7. Wesley will *cogitate* over the problem until…
   he figures out the answer

8. Bill was *elated* to learn that…
   unicorns were real

9. The *licentious* soldier was court-martialed for…
   idk

10. The sheriff arrested the *ruffians* for…
    robbing the bank

11. One *epigram* that applies to hard work is…
    Hard work by Lisa Johnson

12. The mayor *parried* the reporter's difficult questions by…
    changing the subject.

13. It is *fatalistic* to think that you will…
    get into Harvard with really bad grades

14. A *numismatist* might spend his or her evenings…
    counting coins.

15. Myra became *pensive* when Cal told her that she…
    lies to herself.

    her job.

Exercise III

Roots, Prefixes, and Suffixes

Study the entries and answer the questions that follow.

The prefix *pro–* means "before" or "in front."
The roots *fab* and *fess* mean "to speak."
The roots *hab* and *hib* mean "to have" or "to possess."

1. Using *literal* translations as guidance, define the following words without using a dictionary:

    A. ~~inhabit~~   D. ~~affable~~
    B. inhibition   E. ~~confab~~
    C. prohibit   F. fabulist

2. A[n] ___*B*___ is a tendency to repeat a particular behavior and is often difficult to cease. If you have a painting that you want people to see, you might ___*A*___ it in an art gallery.

3. At college, a[n] ___*E*___ might stand in front of a classroom and speak to students. A short story that often features talking animals and a moral is called a[n] ___*D*___ .

4. List as many words as you can think of that contain the prefix *pro–*.

    – protect   – produce
    – promote   – provide

Exercise IV

Inference

Complete the sentence by inferring information about the italicized word from its context.

1. Wayne always *obtrudes* upon our conversations, so if we want to discuss something privately, we should… call each other

2. Two prisoners escaped because the *lackadaisical* guard was… not doing his job

3. Japan is an industrial power, but its *paucity* of natural resources forces the nation to… find resources elsewhere

Exercise V

Writing

Here is a writing prompt similar to the one you will find on the writing portion of an assessment test.

Plan and write an essay based on the following statement:

> The Victorian poet and critic Matthew Arnold said that "the end and aim of all literature" is "a critcism of life."

Assignment: Do you agree or disagree with Arnold's view that literature is, for good or for bad, a criticism of life? Write an essay in which you support or refute Arnold's position. Support your point with evidence from your reading, classroom studies, and experience. Be sure to consider literature in all its forms, including songs, drama, film, television, and poetry.

Thesis: Write a *one-sentence* response to the assignment. Make certain this single sentence offers a clear statement of your position.

Example: Matthew Arnold is right about literature's being a criticism of life because the best literature is that which accurately depicts the good and bad parts of reality.

_____

_____

Organizational Plan: List at least three subtopics you will use to support your main idea. This list is your outline.

1. _____

2. _____

3. _____

Draft: Following your outline, write a good first draft of your essay. Remember to support all your points with examples, facts, references to reading, etc.

Review and Revise: Exchange essays with a classmate. Using the scoring guide for Organization on page 251, score your partner's essay (while he or she scores yours). Focus on the organizational plan and the use of language conventions. If necessary, rewrite your essay to improve the organizational plan and/or your use of language.

Exercise VI

English Practice

Identifying Sentence Errors

Identify the grammatical error in each of the following sentences. If the sentence contains no error, select answer choice E.

1. Her sister and her are now employed at Beef Barn as cooks.   No error
   (A)   (B)   (C)   (D)   (E)

2. While dad slept the toddlers wrote on the walls with crayons.   No error
   (A)   (B)   (C)   (D)   (E)

3. An important function of helicopters are search and rescue
   (A)   (B)   (C)   (D)
   capability.   No error
                    (E)

4. The mechanic told Bill and I that the car was not finished.   No error
   (A)   (B) (C)   (D)   (E)

5. Greg only threw the shot put twenty feet.   No error
   (A) (B) (C)   (D)   (E)

Improving Sentences

The underlined portion of each sentence below contains some flaw. Select the answer choice that best corrects the flaw.

6. Jillian could have cared less about the score of the hockey game.
   A. could haven't cared less
   B. couldn't have cared less
   C. could have cared as much
   D. couldn't have cared more
   E. could care less

7. Going to school is preferable than going to work.
   A. not preferable than
   B. preferable
   C. perforated to
   D. preferable to
   E. preferable, then

8. <u>Wild and vicious, the veterinarian examined the wounded panther.</u>
   A. The wild and vicious wounded panther was examined by the veterinarian.
   B. The veterinarian examined the wounded, wild, and vicious panther.
   C. The vicious veterinarian examined the wild and wounded panther.
   D. Wild and vicious, the examined panther wounded the veterinarian.
   E. The veterinarian examined the wild and vicious panther.

9. <u>Journalists are</u> stimulated by his or her deadline.
   A. A journalist are
   B. Journalism is
   C. Journalists is
   D. A journalist is
   E. Journalists' are

10. When <u>someone has</u> been drinking, they are more likely to speed.
    A. some one has
    B. a person has
    C. a driver has
    D. someone have
    E. drivers have

Lesson Two

1. **prose** (prōz) *n.* ordinary writing or <u>speech</u>, other than poetry or music
Meagan had a talent for writing *prose*, so she routinely won essay contests.
I had to give a prose about the book

2. **renaissance** (re' nə sonts, zonts) *n.* a <u>revival or rebirth</u>, especially in thinking or activity
A *renaissance* of the downtown area changed the abandoned, burned-out buildings into flourishing businesses and luxury apartments.
syn: renewal; reawakening

3. **surcharge** (sur' charj) *n.* a <u>charge</u> added to the usual cost
Tim got annoyed when he had to pay a *surcharge* for Internet access in his hotel room. *The surcharge for this bag was ridiculous.*
ant: discount; refund

4. **enshroud** (en shroud') *v.* to cover up; <u>to conceal</u>
A blanket of fog *enshrouds* the small town in the valley after every spring rain, rendering the houses invisible from the highway on the hill.
syn: hide; cloak

5. **broach** (brōch) *v.* <u>to bring up a subject for discussion</u>
At a funeral, it would be in poor taste to *broach* the subject of the departed's last will and testament.
syn: initiate

6. **amalgamate** (ə mal' gə māt) *v.* to combine
The great leader *amalgamated* many small tribes into his own to make a single, powerful nation.
syn: unite; blend; merge; consolidate   *ant: splinter; disunite*

7. **demented** (di men' tid) *adj.* mentally ill; <u>insane</u>
Mary's *demented* cat attacks anything that makes a noise, including the television.
syn: deranged; insane   *ant: sane*

8. **hone** (hōn) *v.* <u>to sharpen</u>
The butcher used a whetstone to *hone* his knives until they were razor sharp.
ant: dull
I had to hone my flip for the diving meet.

9. **beleaguer** (bi lē′ gər)   *v.*   to besiege by encircling (as with an army); to harass
The mosquitoes will *beleaguer* you if you venture near the swamp.
syn: surround; annoy   *ant: evade*

10. **gorge** (gôrj)   *v.*   to eat or swallow greedily
The beagle *gorged* itself after it chewed through the bag of dog food.

11. **antiquated** (an′ ti kwā tid)   *adj.*   no longer used or useful; very old
The *antiquated* washboard hung on the wall, useful only as a decoration.
syn: obsolete; out-of-date; archaic   *ant: modern*
This chair is so antiquated.

12. **opiate** (ō′ pē it)   *n.*   a narcotic used to cause sleep or bring relief from pain
The veterinarian used an *opiate* to sedate the wounded animal.
                                    ant: stimulant

13. **caricature** (kar′ i kə chûr)   *n.*   an exaggerated portrayal of one's features
The *caricature* of the mayor in the political cartoon magnified the size of his ears and nose.
syn: mockery; cartoon   The caricature makes me look like idiot!

14. **dally** (dal′ ē)   *v.*   to waste time; to dawdle
If you *dally* too long in making a decision, someone else will buy the car you want.   If you dally too long will
syn: dawdle; loiter   fail the test.   *ant: hasten; hurry*

15. **felonious** (fə lō′ nē əs)   *adj.*   pertaining to or constituting a major crime
The inmate expected to be released from prison early, despite the many *felonious* activities on his record.
syn: criminal

The felonious man, took money from his old mother.

Exercise I

Words in Context

From the list below, supply the words needed to complete the paragraph. Some words will not be used.

antiquated	gorge	caricature	felonious
opiate	dally	beleaguer	

1. Alex crouched behind a palm tree and shook her head; she had escaped from her cell, but she was still woozy from the ___opiate___ that her captors used to drug her. She didn't ___dally___ because the guards would be searching for her in a matter of minutes. Knowing that it might be days before she would eat again, Alex ___gorged___ herself on a bag lunch that one of the guards had left unattended near her cell. Seconds later, she began looking for the ___antiquated___ truck that the guards had used to transport her to the compound. She knew that the outmoded vehicle wouldn't set any speed records, but it was her only option for getting back to civilization. The odds were against Alex, but she had to make it out of the jungle before she could expose the kingpin's ___felonious___ operation to the public.

From the list below, supply the words needed to complete the paragraph. Some words will not be used.

dally	caricature	beleaguer	amalgamate
hone	felonious	demented	

2. Doctor Rearick, a famous chemist, mused at the ___caricature___ of himself in the editorial cartoon. The artist had depicted the aging chemist as a[n] ___demented___ scientist, like Victor Frankenstein or Doctor Moreau, at a lab table trying to ___amalgamate___ two mysterious liquids by pouring them both into a steaming test tube. Reporters ___beleaguer___ him with phone calls for days after he announced the discovery of a remarkable new alloy, and Rearick knew that he would need to ___hone___ his public speaking skills before he explained the full significance of the discovery in front of the television news cameras.

From the list below, supply the words needed to complete the paragraph. Some words will not be used.

prose	renaissance	surcharge	dally
broach	enshroud	felonious	

3. Kim gladly paid the ___surcharge___ for keeping the library book for a few extra days. She loved how the ___prose___ of the old journal describes life during the Great War, which had ___enshroud___ the nation in chaos and uncertainty. The author rarely ___broached___ the subject of his own safety or comfort, though he does mention the ___renaissance___ that occurs in his city during the reconstruction after the conflict, when the city becomes a center for science and academics.

Exercise II

Sentence Completion

Complete the sentence in a way that shows you understand the meaning of the italicized vocabulary word.

1. Marci carefully *enshrouded* her new car in a silk cover because...

   She didn't want it to be dirty

2. The restaurant will include a *surcharge* for...

   a refill of drinks.

3. People think that she's *demented* just because she...

   runs around in circles.

4. The struggling nation experienced a *renaissance* when...

   the mayor anouced something big.

5. The seagulls *beleaguered* the people on the beach until...

   the people gave them food.

6. You should first *hone* your skills if you plan to...

   go to the olympics.

7. The teacher told us not to *amalgamate* those chemicals because...

   they would explode.

8. Gail hopes that practicing her *prose* will...

   have her memorize it.

9. Andy's *felonious* behavior finally caught up to him when...

   the police took him to jail.

10. No one wants to *broach* the subject of...

    the divorce.

11. Bert *gorged* himself at the buffet because he...

    was starving

12. The political cartoonist's *caricature* depicted the president as...

    very annoying / a clown

13. If you *dally* in finishing your report, you might...

    have a bad report.

14. The doctor administered an *opiate* to the patient to...

    ease the pain.

15. Paul replaced his *antiquated* computer because it...

    stopped working.

Exercise III

Roots, Prefixes, and Suffixes

Study the entries and answer the questions that follow.

The prefix *sub–* means "under" or "below."
The suffix *–ize* means "to make."
The root *urb* means "city."

1. Using *literal* translations as guidance, define the following words without using a dictionary:

    A. suburb   D. standardize
    B. urbanize   E. subhuman
    C. substandard   F. humanize

2. A[n] _submarine_ is a vessel that travels underwater, and a *subway* train travels _under_ the ground.

3. List as many words as you can think of that contain the prefix *sub–* or the suffix *–ize*.

    urbanize
    indivualize
    standardize

    Summarize

Exercise IV

Inference

Complete the sentence by inferring information about the italicized word from its context.

1. If Kevin needs a large bowl to *amalgamate* the ingredients, he is probably going to…
    use a spoon to mix it.

2. If an angry mob *beleaguered* the driver of the car, then the driver was probably…
    very angry.

3. Nolan went to the library to *hone* his understanding of chemistry by…
    reading textbooks.

Exercise V

Critical Reading

Below is a reading passage followed by several multiple-choice questions. Carefully read the passage and choose the best answer for each of the questions.

The author of the following passage explains recent astronomical discoveries and their significance to humanity.

1   Humans have fantasized about the significance of planets ever since the ancients first identi-fied them as "wandering stars." Planets are fundamental to mythology and astrology, and as we indulge our imaginations with the future of humanity, planets are essential to our visions of interstellar endeavors, both in fiction and in fact. Recent discoveries have revealed plenty of new material for us to **gorge** our imaginations on. Our civilization may lack the technology to set foot on the seven unexplored planets of our own solar system, but that shouldn't prevent us from compiling a list of new planets to explore when we finally do have the technology.

2   In 1991, Aleksander Wolszczan, an astronomy professor from Penn State University, used a radio telescope to time signals that revealed three planets orbiting a very distant pulsar. Located more than 1,000 light years from Earth in the constellation Virgo, two of the planets resemble Earth in density, while the third is moon-sized. The probability of life on the planets is low; due to their proximity to the pulsar, the planets are **enshrouded** in radiation that renders them inhos-pitable to life as we know it. The planets are probably barren, lifeless worlds, but such speculation is only secondary to the paramount discovery: Planets exist elsewhere in the galaxy. Their simple existence is enough to confirm that our own solar system is only one of the possible billions in the galaxy—and we have the means to detect them.

3   The next major extrasolar planet discovery occurred in 1995, when Michel Mayor and Didier Queloz used spectrographic data to discover a large planet orbiting 51 Pegasi, a star that resembles our own sun. The planet is likely a gas giant similar to Jupiter, but its correlation with a sun-like star inspired high hopes that a solar system like our own will eventually be found.

4   Since 1995, astronomers have added more than 900 new planets to their list of discov-eries, some of which exist in multiple-planet systems. Most of the discovered planets are Jovian, like that of the 51 Pegasi system, but that, astronomers stress, is due to our limited detection methods.

5   Exoplanets are invisible to **antiquated** optical telescopes. Radio telescopes allow researchers to rely upon the behavior of parent stars to signal the presence of planets. As any planet orbits a star, the two bodies pull themselves toward each other due to gravity. For an observer who has a side view of the celestial process, the parent star will appear to "wobble." All stars with planets exhibit this behavior, but large planets that orbit close to their parent stars cause enough wobble that we can detect it from hundreds, thousands, or millions of light years away. By identifying and measuring the wobble of the parent stars, astronomers confirm the presence of planets and calculate planetary mass.

6   Discoveries become increasingly noteworthy as astronomers refine extrasolar detection tech-niques. At the time in which the first pulsar planets were discovered, researchers found mainly gas giants near the parent stars, but are now discovering planetary systems that contain increas-ingly smaller planets with longer orbits. The significance? As we discover planetary systems with smaller planets farther from their parent stars, we approach the day in which we find the smaller planets: terrestrial planets, like Earth. Where terrestrial planets exist, conditions for known forms of life could exist. The discovery of extraterrestrial life could be a **renaissance** for the attention, philosophies, and endeavors of our civilization.

7 Even if we are unable to find any terrestrial planets, astronomers theorize that our next major extrasolar discovery might be that of planetary satellites. If the Jovian planets that have been discovered are anything like Jupiter and Saturn, then there is a probability that they will have satellites—Jupiter has sixty-seven known satellites, and Saturn has at least sixty-two. Some of the satellites in our solar system, such as Saturn's Titan and Jupiter's Io, have atmospheres. The satellite atmospheres in our solar system might be inhospitable to life, but what about the satellites of newly discovered giants?

8 Is it possible that a satellite of one of the newly discovered planets, 326 light years away, could have atmospheric conditions like those of our nurturing Earth? Time and technology will tell, but at least we now know, thanks to early extrasolar explorers, where to direct our attention in the human quest for answers.

1A. The primary purpose of this passage is to
  A. offer theories on the formation of planets.
  B. explain how new planets are detected.
  C. discuss the impact of new discoveries.
  D. dispute heliocentric theory.
  E. inform readers about the discovery of new planets.

1B. Which type of support best contributes to the purpose of the passage, as answered in question 1A?
  A. arguments against the usefulness of the discoveries
  B. comparison between mythology and astrology
  C. questions throughout the passage
  D. details about terrestrial planets beyond the solar system
  E. synopsis of major extrasolar planet discoveries

2A. The overall tone of this passage is
  A. descriptive.
  B. humorous.
  C. speculative.
  D. optimistic.
  E. simplistic.

2B. Which detail contributes most to establishing the tone of the passage?
  A. critiques of the reluctance to find new exoplanets
  B. descriptions of the scientific gains from finding new planets
  C. speculation about the future of extrasolar discoveries
  D. the likelihood of satellites orbiting Jovian planets
  E. the concept of studying star behavior to locate planets

3A. Which of the following would be the best substitute for *proximity* in paragraph 2?
  A. size
  B. aloofness
  C. remoteness
  D. gravitational pull
  E. closeness

3B. How would the context change if *proximity* were replaced with the synonym used as the answer to question 3A?
   A.   The change would add personality to the search for planets.
   B.   The new context would sound less formal than the original context.
   C.   The context would better support the formal tone of the passage.
   D.   The context would have a more scientific tone.
   E.   The change would alter the meaning of the context significantly.

4A. According to paragraph 2, why is it unimportant that the pulsar planets are probably devoid of life?
   A.   The pulsar bombards the planets with radiation.
   B.   The inherent value is the discovery of the planets.
   C.   The planets lack atmospheres, like our own moon.
   D.   Life has not yet been detected on the planets.
   E.   The planets rotate too quickly and offer no possibility of colonization.

4B. According to the same paragraph, the barren, lifeless planets should not be regarded negatively because
   A.   they are not worth investigating until we can make better observations.
   B.   they are still possibly inhabited by higher orders of microbes.
   C.   they have little value, and we are not ready to mine them.
   D.   they are proof enough that planets exist outside our own solar system.
   E.   they can support life, even without a sun similar to our own.

5A. As used in paragraph 4, the word *Jovian* most nearly means
   A.   very distant.
   B.   primarily mythological.
   C.   resembling Jupiter.
   D.   nonexistent.
   E.   both large and small.

5B. *Jovian* planets can also be described as being
   A.   extrasolar.
   B.   terrestrial.
   C.   binary.
   D.   satellites.
   E.   gaseous.

6A. According to paragraph 5, astronomers discover primarily large planets because
   A.   Earth has no "optical telescopes" beyond the atmosphere.
   B.   small planets do not cause enough "wobble" to detect from Earth.
   C.   small planets don't offer a "side view."
   D.   the atmospheres of small planets "orbit close" enough to obscure the images.
   E.   "parent stars" are too bright to allow observations.

6B. Astronomers use the word *detect* instead of *see* because
   A.   no one actually sees the extrasolar planets; they are viewed indirectly.
   B.   the planets are heard through audible radio signals.
   C.   finding planets requires detective work.
   D.   *detect* is a more formal word suitable for science writing.
   E.   the planets cannot be seen without a telescope.

7.   In paragraph 7, the author lists the known quantities of satellites for Jupiter and Saturn with the purpose of
   A.   increasing the likelihood that the new planets will have satellites.
   B.   providing the audience with statistics to support the theory.
   C.   describing how Jupiter and Saturn are unlike the discovered planets.
   D.   providing an example that supports the new planets' having satellites.
   E.   emphasizing the argument for space exploration.

8A. Which of the following best describes this passage?
   A.   specific and explanatory
   B.   conjectural and cynical
   C.   abridged and speculative
   D.   thorough and comprehensive
   E.   researched and scholarly

8B. The organization of this passage is best described as
   A.   pros and cons.
   B.   chronological.
   C.   compare and contrast.
   D.   narrative.
   E.   step-by-step.

9A. What would make the best title for this passage?
   A.   Techniques of Planetary Detection
   B.   Planets Like Jupiter
   C.   The Search for Life
   D.   The Space Frontier: Specks on the Horizon
   E.   Astronomers Find Planets

9B. Which choice best explains the irony of the word *explorers* in paragraph 8?
   A.   The explorers mentioned have travelled light years to detect extrasolar planets.
   B.   The explorers are essentially blind, because extrasolar planets are invisible to optical telescopes.
   C.   None of the extrasolar planets are proven to exist because we cannot get to them.
   D.   Extrasolar planet explorers do not actually leave Earth to explore.
   E.   The explorers are actually computers and robots—not human beings.

10A. This passage would most likely be found in a/an
   A.   encyclopedia.
   B.   fiction novel.
   C.   history book.
   D.   book about new astronomy techniques.
   E.   exploration magazine.

10B. Which detail of the passage helps to establish an informal tone?
   A.   the explanation of astronomical terms
   B.   the combination of biographical data with scientific observations
   C.   the questions to the audience
   D.   the certainty of the discoveries
   E.   the heavy use of slang terms

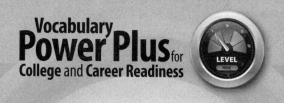
Lesson Three

1. **insurrection** (in sə rek´ shən) *n.* a rebellion against established authority
   or government
   During the *insurrection*, the rebels captured every relative of the ruling family and
   either exiled or executed them.
   syn: revolt; uprising   *ant: compliance*

2. **thesis** (thē´ sis) *n.* a proposed idea that has yet to be proven
   It took Lacey a full month to write her senior English *thesis* on the significance
   of fish in the works of Henry David Thoreau.
   syn: proposition; theory

3. **maul** (môl) *v.* to injure by beating and rough treatment
   The grizzly bear *mauled* Kelly until she remembered to stop screaming and play dead,
   which convinced the animal to leave her alone.
   syn: batter   She   got   mauled by a dog.

4. **deliberate** (di lib´ ə rāt) *v.* to consider carefully, especially as a group
   The jury *deliberated* for only thirty minutes before agreeing on the verdict.
   syn: ponder; meditate

5. **forum** (fôr´ əm) *n.* a meeting or meeting place for public discussion
   The university provides a *forum* where new students can talk to older students and
   ask questions about life on campus.
   syn: assembly; conference The forum was 6 hours
   away so I decided 2 fly there.

6. **edifice** (ed´ ə fis) *n.* a large, elaborate structure; an imposing building
   The palace was not just a home; it was an *edifice* that created envy among
   foreign rulers.
   syn: fortress The edifice was *ant: hovel* magnificient.

7. **ambidextrous** (am bi dek´ strəs) *adj.* equally skillful with either hand
   The *ambidextrous* woman could write both left- and right-handed.
   She is ambidextrous so she can w/ write
   both hands.

8. **belated** (bi lā´ tid) *adj.* delayed
   Joan sent a *belated* birthday card to her sister.
   syn: tardy; late Happy belated birfday. *ant: timely*

9. **animate** (an´ ə māt) *v.* to give life or motion to
   A trip to the ice cream parlor helped to *animate* the sullen child.
   syn: enliven; encourage; excite   *ant: quell*
   The man was animated when
   he saw the large
   stack of cash.

10. **knead** (nēd) *v.* to work dough or clay into a uniform mixture
It is easier to *knead* dough with an electric mixer than by hand.
syn: squeeze; rub; press   *She kneaded the dough*

11. **chauvinist** (shō′ və nist) *n.* one having a fanatical devotion to a country, gender, or religion, and displaying contempt for other countries, the opposite sex, or other beliefs
He did not dislike women, but he was a *chauvinist* when it came to hiring women for management positions.

12. **egalitarian** (i gal i târ′ ē ən) *adj.* promoting equal rights for all people
The equal rights amendment for women was founded on *egalitarian* principles.
   The egalitarian government   *ant: elitist*
   makes new laws constantly.

13. **berserk** (bər sûrk′, zûrk) *adj.* in a state of violent or destructive rage
My father almost went *berserk* when I told him I had dented his new car.
syn: frenzied   *She went*   *ant: placid; complacent*
   berserk over losing her job.

14. **ostentatious** (os ten tā′ shəs) *adj.* marked by a conspicuous, showy, or pretentious display
The *ostentatious* charity ball cost the guests $2,000 a plate.
syn: grandiose   *ant: unobtrusive; bland*

15. **delude** (di lōōd′) *v.* to mislead; to fool
The fast-talking salesman could not *delude* us into buying the dilapidated truck.
syn: deceive   *ant: enlighten*

Exercise I

Words in Context

From the list below, supply the words needed to complete the paragraph. Some words will not be used.

delude	forum	~~edifice~~	berserk
~~ostentatious~~	~~animate~~		

1. The old Lane estate was a[n] _edific_ that towered over the other homes in the neighborhood. It had a[n] _ostentags&us_ courtyard more suitable for a palace, and rows of shimmering Aspen trees seemed to _animate_ the grounds when they fluttered with even the mildest breeze. The elaborate exterior of the mansion might _delude_ someone into thinking that the house must be beautiful inside, but in actuality, the roof leaks, the paint is peeling, and the floors creak.

From the list below, supply the words needed to complete the paragraph. Some words will not be used.

~~chauvinist~~	belated	maul	~~egalitarian~~
ostentatious			

2. The corporation claimed to endorse _egalitarian_ company policies, but some of the managers were _chauvinist_ who refused to promote anyone not native to Scandinavia. One of the foreign employees eventually filed suit against the company, and in two years, was awarded the _belated_ promotion he had long deserved.

From the list below, supply the words needed to complete the paragraph. Some words will not be used.

~~berserk~~	delude	~~knead~~	edifice
ambidextrous			

3. Laurie _kneaded_ the modeling clay until it was soft enough to work with. Since her work required deep concentration, she nearly went _berserk_ when her assistant interrupted for the third time to obtain Laurie's signature. Even though Laurie was _ambidextrous_ she could not sign her name and focus on her art simultaneously.

From the list below, supply the words needed to complete the paragraph. Some words will not be used.

thesis	~~maul~~	animate	~~insurrection~~
~~deliberate~~	egalitarian	~~forum~~	

4. Though the King of Spamistan wanted to _maul_ the rebels personally and be finished with the matter, his advisor convinced him that such violent measures would surely incite a[n] _insurrection_ Prominent Spamistanian subjects had recently held a[n] _forum_ in which they _deliberated_ over ideas about changes to the new government. They concluded with the _thesis_ that the king would need to cede authority for the nation to succeed.

Exercise II

Sentence Completion

Complete the sentence in a way that shows you understand the meaning of the italicized vocabulary word.

1. Janet bought a *belated* graduation gift for Mike because she...
   missed his graduation.
2. The *ambidextrous* pitcher could throw...
   w/ both hands.
3. In trying to open it, Dawn *mauled* the bag of pretzels so much that...
   the pretzels flew everywhere,
4. In an *egalitarian* nation, everyone has the...
   right to believe what they want to.
5. One *edifice* that most people have seen in pictures is...
   the White House.
6. The soccer player *kneaded* her calf muscle because...
   she hurt it.
7. Though he was quite wealthy, the miser's home lacked *ostentatious* artwork or furniture because he... thought it was too much to look at.
8. The dance *forum* is a good place for...
   a meeting.
9. The sound of food pouring into a metal dish *animated*...
   the starving guest.
10. Uncle Phil was admittedly a male *chauvinist* who believed that...
    women were dumb.
11. Don't let the resort's brochure *delude* you; we went there last year, and the pictures in the guide are... not a good representation of what they look like.
12. Rabies caused the dog to act *berserk*, so...
    it got put down.
13. To stop the *insurrection*, the king decided to...
    get his troops to fight back.
14. The most interesting *thesis* at the science fair was...
    that cake is healthier than pizza.
15. Liz wants to *deliberate* for a while before...
    making a desicion.

Exercise III

Roots, Prefixes, and Suffixes

Study the entries and answer the questions that follow.

The roots *mater* and *matr* mean "mother."
The root *micro* means "small."
The root *meter* means "measure."
The root *aut* means "self."

1. Using *literal* translations as guidance, define the following words without using a dictionary:

    A. alma mater   D. microprocessor
    B. matron   E. micrometer
    C. matrimony   F. automatic

2. Mothers are known to have certain _____ instincts, especially with regard to caring for their children. In a *matriarchal* society, family lineage is traced through the _____'s side of the family instead of the father's side.

3. If *cosmos* means "world," then a *microcosm* must be _____. Microbes are so _____ that you need a[n] _____ to see them.

4. List as many words as you can think of that contain the roots *meter* or *auto*.

Exercise IV

Inference

Complete the sentence by inferring information about the italicized word from its context.

1. If the mad doctor wants to try to *animate* the lifeless monster, then he or she wants to...

2. An *ambidextrous* golfer would not need to worry about having left- or right-handed clubs because...

3. If Karen was angry that Mark did not follow through with his *egalitarian* plan, then Mark must have...

Exercise V

Writing

Here is a writing prompt similar to the one you will find on the writing portion of an assessment test.

Plan and write an essay based on the following statement:

> The happiest day in all my outer life!
>
> For in an old shed full of tools and lumber at the end of the garden, and half-way between an empty fowl-house and a disused stable (each an Eden in itself) I found a small toy-wheelbarrow—quite the most extraordinary, the most unheard of and undreamed of, humorously, daintily, exquisitely fascinating object I had ever come across in all my brief existence.
>
> –George du Maurier, *Peter Ibbetson* (1891)

Assignment: Your opinion of what was extraordinary during your youth might be quite different from that of George du Maurier's wheelbarrow. In an essay, explain something that was "unheard of, undreamed of" or "exquisitely fascinating" when you were a child. Explain where you found it and what it meant to you. Compare this object to things that you hold as important today and explain their significance in your life. Support your idea with evidence from your reading, classroom studies, experience, and observation.

Thesis: Write a *one-sentence* response to the assignment. Make certain this single sentence offers a clear statement of your position.

Example: The object of fascination during my youth, which still captivates me today, is a secluded cave deep in the forest that I discovered while on a camping trip.

_____

_____

Organizational Plan: List at least three subtopics you will use to support your main idea. This list is your outline.

1. _____

2. _____

3. _____

Draft: Following your outline, write a good first draft of your essay. Remember to support all of your points with examples, facts, references to reading, etc.

Review and Revise: Exchange essays with a classmate. Using the scoring guide for Development on page 252, score your partner's essay (while he or she scores yours). Focus on the development of ideas and the use of language conventions. If necessary, rewrite your essay to incorporate more (or more relevant) support and/or improve your use of language.

Exercise VI

Improving Paragraphs

Read the following passage and then choose the best revision for the underlined portions of the paragraph. The questions will require you to make decisions regarding the revision of the reading selection. Some revisions are not of actual mistakes, but will improve the clarity of the writing.

[1]

We have tried in the <u>proceeding</u>[1] chapters to understand a few of the laws of health and to apply them intelligently to our daily living. It will help us to clinch what we have already mastered, if <u>we supplement our work with a knowledge of simple methods now</u>[2] of procedure in case of the more common and not as serious accidents and emergencies.

1. A. NO CHANGE
   B. progressing
   C. succeeding
   D. preceding

2. F. NO CHANGE
   G. we now supplement our work with a knowledge of simple methods
   H. we supplement our work with a knowledge now of simple methods
   J. we supplement now our work with a knowledge of simple methods

[2]

Emergencies and accidents are a frequent occurrence. A playmate may cut his leg or foot with a scythe or knife, or fall and <u>have broken</u>[3] his arm. A child may accidentally swallow some laudanum, set his own clothing on fire, or push a bean into his nose or <u>ear, a teamster</u>[4] may be brought in with his ears frostbitten. A small boy may fall into the river and be brought out apparently drowned. One of our own family may suddenly be taken sick with some contagious disease or <u>may be</u>[5] suffocated by coal gas.

3. A. NO CHANGE
   B. break
   C. broke
   D. breaking

4. F. NO CHANGE
   G. ear a teamster
   H. ear—a teamster
   J. ear. A teamster

5. A. NO CHANGE
   B. might become
   C. will be
   D. might

[3]

All these and many other things of a like nature call for a cool head, a steady hand, <u>and, some practical knowledge</u>[6] of what is to be done until medical or surgical help <u>was obtained.</u>[7] A fairly good working knowledge of such matters may be easily mastered.

6. F. NO CHANGE
    G. and, some practical knowledge,
    H. and some practical knowledge
    J. and; some practical knowledge

7. A. NO CHANGE
    B. is been obtained
    C. gets obtained
    D. is obtained

[4]

A boy or girl who has acquired this knowledge and <u>who are able</u>[8] to maintain a certain amount of self-control will find many opportunities in later years <u>for to lend</u>[9] a hand in the midst of accidents or sudden sickness.

8. F. NO CHANGE
    G. whom are able
    H. is
    J. who is able

9. A. NO CHANGE
    B. to lend
    C. of to lend
    D. to the lending

[5]

(1) All that is expected of us is to wait until the doctor comes. (2) Retain, as far as possible, presence of mind, or, <u>another words,</u>[10] keep cool. (3) Act <u>prompt and quiet,</u>[11] but not with haste. (4) First aid kits have been manufactured since 1890, at the latest.

10. F. NO CHANGE
    G. an other words
    H. in another words
    J. in other words

11. A. NO CHANGE
    B. promptly and quiet
    C. promptly and quietly
    D. prompt and quietly

12. Which sentence should be deleted from paragraph 5 because it deviates from the flow of information?
    F. sentence (1)
    G. sentence (2)
    H. sentence (3)
    J. sentence (4)

[6]

(1) Make the sufferer comfortable by <u>providing</u>[13] an abundance of fresh air and placing him in a restful position. (2) Loosen all tight articles of clothing. (3) Such as belts, bindings, corsets, and collars. (4) Be sure to send for a doctor at once if the emergency calls for any such skilled service.

13. A. NO CHANGE
    B. giving the sufferer
    C. them
    D. providing them with

14. In the final paragraph, sentence 3 requires revision because
    F. it contains an unnecessary comma in the series.
    G. it is a fragment, not a sentence.
    H. all the nouns should be singular.
    J. it needs a semicolon.

Review Lessons 1-3

Exercise I

Inferences

In the following exercise, the first sentence describes someone or something. Infer information from the first sentence, and then choose the word from the Word Bank that best completes the second sentence.

egalitarian	chauvinist	paucity	antiquated
beleaguer	felonious	gall	ambidextrous

1. The major league batter could hit right-handed as well as he could hit left-handed, which made it difficult for pitchers to adapt to him.

   From this sentence, we can infer that the batter is _____.

2. The electric typewriter for sale at the flea market had a price tag of $1.00, even though it had cost $300.00 when brand new in 1987.

   From this sentence, we can infer that the typewriter is _____.

3. The company's hiring policy states that hiring practices are not influenced by race, gender, religion, or ethnicity.

   From this sentence, we can infer that the company has _____ hiring practices.

4. The treasurer was sentenced to eight months in prison for using the town's tax revenue to remodel her own summer beach house.

   From this sentence, we can infer that the treasurer's _____ behavior landed her in jail.

5. Mort complained about changes to the club rules until they proved to be wildly successful, and then he took full credit for the changes.

   From this sentence, we can infer that Mort has a lot of _____ for taking credit for things he didn't do.

Exercise II

Related Words

Some of the vocabulary words from Lessons 1 through 3 have related meanings. Complete the following sentences by choosing the word that best fits the context, based on information you infer from the use of the italicized word. Some word pairs will be antonyms, some will be synonyms, and some will simply be words often used in the same context.

1. Only one celebrity had the *gall* to drive his _____, bright yellow $300,000 supercar to the charity benefit for the poor.
    A. pensive
    B. demented
    C. ambidextrous
    D. egalitarian
    E. ostentatious

2. The two *ruffians* who started a riot downtown were thrown in jail for their _____ actions.
    A. lackadaisical
    B. antiquated
    C. fatalistic
    D. deliberate
    E. felonious

3. The king alienated the last of his loyal subjects when, during an economic depression, he commissioned the construction of a massive marble *edifice* as his summer home, an act of vanity that ignited a[n] _____ that ended with his exile.
    A. epigram
    B. thesis
    C. opiate
    D. insurrection
    E. paucity

4. The emperor used falsified news stories to _____ the public into believing in fictional enemies, while his Department of Information *enshrouded* the population in ignorance by cutting off all Internet access to the world beyond their borders.
    A. delude
    B. obtrude
    C. dally
    D. cogitate
    E. broach

5. A scientific breakthrough caused a[n] _____ in the company's *antiquated* methods of production.
    A. renaissance
    B. gorge
    C. insurrection
    D. prose
    E. numismatist

6. During the international _____ to discuss nuclear waste, representatives of several nations *deliberated* over the facts.
    A. opiate
    B. edifice
    C. forum
    D. renaissance
    E. caricature

7. Faced with a difficult life decision, the *pensive* student left the noise of town to be alone on the mountain, where he could _____ in quiet solitude and arrive at a solution to his problem.
    A. dally
    B. alienate
    C. cogitate
    D. knead
    E. amalgamate

8. The younger sailors feared what might *transpire* during the voyage after the superstitious old deckhand provided a[n] _____ interpretation of events that had taken place that day.
    A. felonious
    B. egalitarian
    C. fatalistic
    D. pensive
    E. antiquated

9. Amber knew her *lackadaisical* brother would _____ and show up late to the recital, so she told him it started an hour earlier than it actually did.
    A. surcharge
    B. dally
    C. alienate
    D. delude
    E. animate

10. The author's funny _____ was delightful to read, especially in the way it portrayed the eccentric townsfolk as hilarious *caricatures* of their real-life counterparts.
    A. paucity
    B. forum
    C. opiate
    D. prose
    E. thesis

Deeper Meanings

Choose a word to replace the italicized word in each sentence. All of the possible choices for each sentence have similar definitions, but the correct answer will have a connotation that best suits the context. For example, the words "delete," "destroy," and "obliterate" all mean "to remove or wipe out," but no one would ever say, "I destroyed the name from the document." The correct choice will be the word that has the best specific meaning and does not render the sentence awkward in tone or content. When choices seem close, look for a clue in the context that makes one choice better than the other.

Note that the correct answer is not always the primary vocabulary word from the lesson.

ostentatious	corny	felonious	brilliant	important
devoured	skinny	decorated	ignored	horrible
cadaverous	nibbled	beautiful	demented	fashionable

1. Jill felt that the police should spend more time investigating *mean* crimes than writing traffic citations.

    Better word: _____

2. The *wacky* scientist had no qualms about using human beings as test subjects for his latest toxic nerve-agent formula.

    Better word: _____

3. Bones protruded from the rescued girl's *slim* face and torso, making it obvious that she had not eaten in weeks.

    Better word: _____

4. Few of the restaurant customers were especially hungry, so they simply *consumed* their salads.

    Better word: _____

5. James wore a[n] *fancy* coat made of exotic leather covered with hundreds of rhinestones which served no purpose other than attracting attention and increasing the price of the jacket.

    Better word: _____

Exercise IV

Crossword Puzzle

Use the clues to complete the crossword puzzle. The answers consist of vocabulary words from Lessons 1 through 3.

Across

4. a little extra on the bill
9. If you _____ pictures, they become cartoons.
10. fool into believing
12. one who welcomes change
14. on the level
16. righty and lefty
17. quiet and sad
18. to un-friend

Down

1. "We don't stand a chance!"
2. tough guy
3. pig out
5. sharpen
6. waste time
7. Who cares?
8. nicer way to say "late"
11. mad as a hatter
13. criminal
15. stick your nose into

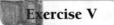

Exercise V

Subject Prompts

Here is a writing prompt similar to the one you will find on the writing portion of an assessment test. Follow the instructions below and write a brief, efficient essay.

Increases in childhood allergies to food have resulted in some schools banning the possession of traditional lunch food, most popularly peanut butter, citing the possibly deadly consequences if it were to come into contact with an allergic student and the proper treatment is not provided quickly enough. Because peanut butter is such a long-lived and popular product, the bans are always controversial, generating complaints from angry parents over the changing of school policies for the accommodation of a very small percentage of students. Those who disagree with the bans suggest that the affected students change their own routines to protect themselves from allergens rather than force changes upon the majority.

Are peanut bans, or equivalent bans, fair practice for schools, or should allergies or similar maladies be handled at the individual level, as the critics suggest? Should the majority be inconvenienced to protect the few, or should the few be assured that they will be provided a safe environment no matter what the cost to others?

Take a side in the argument and write a letter to your school board in favor of or against food bans. Support your argument with at least three subtopics. Your support can be based on your own experience, reading, observations, or reasoning.

Thesis: Write a *one-sentence* response to the above assignment. Make certain this single sentence offers a clear statement of your position.

Example: While the practice seems unfair to the majority, bans are necessary when they involve life-and-death situations.

_____

_____

Organizational Plan: List at least three subtopics you will use to support your main idea. This list is your outline.

1. _____

2. _____

3. _____

Draft: Following your outline, write a good first draft of your essay. Remember to support all your points with examples, facts, references to reading, etc.

Review and Revise: Exchange essays with a classmate. Using the scoring guide for Organization on page 251, score your partner's essay (while he or she scores yours). Focus on the organizational plan and the use of language conventions. If necessary, rewrite your essay to improve the organizational plan and/or your use of language.

Lesson Four

1. **composite** (kom po′ zit) *adj.* <u>made up of separate parts</u>
   In addition to wood, the *composite* bows of Mongolian horse archers were built with
   animal horn and sinew. *~The ~~corn~~ smoothie*
   syn: compound; blended *is composite.*   *ant: uniform; simple*

2. **navigable** (na′ və gə bəl) *adj.* able to be passed or traversed, especially
   for ships *~The ship is navigable~*
   The city on the *navigable* river became a port for merchant ships from throughout the
   region.
   syn: passable; negotiable   *ant: obstructed; inaccessible*

3. **accentuate** (ak sen′ choo āt) *v.* to emphasize
   Pinstripes *accentuate* the sleek, flowing lines of the new model of luxury car.
   syn: stress; accent   *ant: minimize*

4. **transcribe** (tran skrīb′) *v.* <u>to write out or copy information</u>, <u>usually by hand</u>
   No cameras or recorders were allowed in the office, so Frank *transcribed* the
   governor's answers to the reporters' questions.

5. **fruition** (frōō i′ shən) *n.* the attainment or <u>completion of something desired</u>
   If Dr. Insano's evil plan comes to *fruition*, he will be in control of the entire world's
   water supply.
   syn: realization; fulfillment   *ant: loss*

6. **elude** (i lōōd′) *v.* to escape notice; to get away from
   The prisoner tried to *elude* the guards by hiding in the laundry truck.
   syn: avoid; evade; lose *~8 The~ ~criminal~ eluded*
   ~the police because~ ~of his~ high   *ant: attract*

7. **fallow** (fal′ ō) *adj.* inactive; unproductive   *jumping*
   A *fallow* mind needs to be stimulated with challenging ideas and projects.   *skills.*
   syn: idle; barren   *ant: fertile; productive*

8. **blight** (blīt) *n.* <u>anything that destroys</u>, prevents growth, or causes devaluation
   The junkyard was a *blight* on the otherwise appealing neighborhood.
   syn: affliction; disease   *ant: enhancement*

9. **obsequy** (ob′ sə kwē) *n.* <u>a funeral rite or ceremony</u>
   The explorers held brief *obsequies* for their fallen leader before burying him on the
   side of the mountain.

10. **denizen**　(den´ i zən)　*n.*　<u>an occupant</u>; an inhabitant
   Prairie dogs are *denizens* of the Great Plains, so it is unlikely that you would see one in Maine.
   syn: resident　　　　　　　　　　　　*ant: emigrant; alien*

11. **fealty**　(fē´ əl tē)　*n.*　<u>obligated loyalty or faithfulness</u>
   Peasants who did not show any *fealty* to the duke often disappeared.
   syn: devotion; fidelity; allegiance　　　*ant: disloyalty; treachery*

   [handwritten: The crew & odysseus had a fealty w/ each other.]

12. **entice**　(en tīs´)　*v.*　<u>to attract</u> by offering <u>reward or pleasure</u>
   The styling and color of the gown *enticed* me, but I could not afford such an extravagant purchase.
   syn: tempt; lure　　　　　　　　　　*ant: discourage*

   [handwritten: She enticed the little boy w/ candy.]

13. **gratify**　(grat´ ə fī)　*v.*　<u>to please</u>
   To *gratify* the pouting child, his mother handed him a lollipop.
   syn: satisfy; indulge　　　　　　　　*ant: displease; disappoint*

14. **laggard**　(lag´ ərd)　*n.*　a <u>slow person</u>, especially one who falls behind
   Wear proper shoes on the hike, or you'll be a *laggard* and delay the entire group.
   syn: straggler; dawdler　　　　　　　*ant: leader*

15. **gambit**　(gam´ bit)　*n.*　a <u>maneuver or action used to gain an advantage</u>
   The general's *gambit* sacrificed many soldiers, but ultimately won the battle.
   syn: strategy; ploy; maneuver　　　　*ant: blunder*

Exercise I

Words in Context

From the list below, supply the words needed to complete the paragraph. Some words will not be used.

fealty	**entice**	**elude**	**fallow**
blight	**denizen**	**gambit**	

1. Overuse of the soil and an extended drought contributed to the _____ known in history as the Dust Bowl. In the Midwest, _____ fields lay barren for a decade, forcing many _____ of the community to give up their farms and seek employment in the cities, where industry _____ them with promises of steady, but ultimately minuscule, paychecks. In the years that followed the Dust Bowl, farmers stopped over-plowing fields because they knew that no one could _____ nature's wrath.

From the list below, supply the words needed to complete the paragraph. Some words will not be used.

laggard	**entice**	**gambit**	**obsequy**
denizen	**fealty**	**gratify**	

2. The king knew that his plan for a surprise attack would be a[n] _____ that would test the _____ of his soldiers, but it was the only chance he had of thwarting the invading fleet. Speed would be the key to success; one _____ in the ranks could jeopardize the entire operation if the soldier were not in place at the right time. As an incentive to fight well, the king promised to _____ each soldier with twenty acres of land after the battle. The promise was unprecedented, but on the other hand, if the army should fail, then the soldiers would be lucky to receive proper _____ because the invaders did not plan to take prisoners.

From the list below, supply the words needed to complete the paragraph. Some words will not be used.

navigable	**denizen**	**composite**	**fruition**
accentuate	**transcribe**	**fallow**	

3. When their latest design came to _____, five nautical engineers met to test the assembled prototype. Long, thin pinstripes _____ the smooth curves of the new _____ boat, a twin-hulled catamaran constructed of lightweight carbon fiber and aluminum alloy. On smooth, _____ seas, the sleek ship can cruise almost twice the maximum speed of a single-hulled ship of the same weight. As soon as the engineers _____ their notes into a user's manual, they plan to put the design on the open market.

Exercise II

Sentence Completion

Complete the sentence in a way that shows you understand the meaning of the italicized vocabulary word.

1. The ten-year-old boy's curiosity about astronomy was finally *gratified* when…

2. The oil spill was a *blight* that caused…

3. The villagers had limited *fealty* for the new king because he…

4. Tim tried to *elude* the mosquitoes by…

5. Mikhail's *gambit* during the chess game cost him…

6. Many *denizens* of the beach community like to…

7. The *laggard* didn't get tickets to the concert because he…

8. The brochure *enticed* Annette to visit the island because…

9. The *fallow* economy forced many investors to…

10. Instead of a typical *obsequy*, the dying man requested…

11. The *composite* report provides information on both…

12. If the steamboat captain fails to find a *navigable* river, then…

13. You must clearly *accentuate* words when talking to Grandpa because…

14. The archaeologist quickly *transcribed*…

15. When the bridge project reaches *fruition*, the local population will…

Exercise III

Roots, Prefixes, and Suffixes

Study the entries and answer the questions that follow.

The root *chroma* means "color."
The prefix *mono–* means "one."
The prefix *poly–* means "many."
The root *morph* means "form" or "shape."

1. Using *literal* translations as guidance, define the following words without using a dictionary:

   A. polychromatic   D. polymorphic
   B. monochromatic   E. monorail
   C. polygon   F. monosyllabic

2. Someone who speaks in a single pitch, whose voice does not raise or lower, is said to speak in a[n] _____. An activity might become *monotonous* after a few hours if it involves doing only _____ thing.

3. List as many words as you can think of that contain the prefix *poly–* or the root *morph*.

Exercise IV

Inference

Complete the sentence by inferring information about the italicized word from its context.

1. The team would have won the relay race if it had not been for the *laggard* who...

2. The coach's *gambit* left his players vulnerable, but the bold move...

3. If Lonnie tried to *elude* his friends in the mall, then he probably...

Exercise V

Critical Reading

Below is a pair of reading passages followed by several multiple-choice questions. Carefully read the passages and choose the best answer for each of the questions.

The following passages are two famous military speeches intended to motivate soldiers fighting over the same piece of land: northern Italy. Hannibal, the renowned Carthaginian general, delivered the first speech shortly after his army astonished the Romans by crossing the Alps. The second passage includes two speeches from Napoleon Bonaparte. In the first part of the passage, Napoleon addresses his troops as they prepare to enter Italy. In the second part, Napoleon's troops are about to take the city of Milan.

Passage 1

Hannibal's Speech to his Soldiers (218 B.C.)

If, soldiers, you shall by and by, in judging of your own fortune, preserve the same feelings which you experienced a little before in the example of the fate of the others, we have already conquered; for neither was that merely a spectacle, but, as it were, a certain representation of your condition. And I know not whether fortune has not thrown around you still stron-
5　ger chains and more urgent necessities than around your captives. On the right and left two seas enclose you, without your possessing even a single ship for escape. The river Po around you, the Po larger and more impetuous than the Rhone; the Alps behind, scarcely passed by you when fresh and vigorous, hem you in.

　　Here, soldiers, where you have first met the enemy, you must conquer or die; and the
10　same fortune which has imposed the necessity of fighting holds out to you, if victorious, rewards than which men are not wont to desire greater, even from the immortal gods. If we were only about to recover by our valor Sicily and Sardinia, wrested from our fathers, the recompense would be sufficiently ample; but whatever, acquired and amassed by so many triumphs, the Romans possess, all with its masters themselves, will become yours. To gain this
15　rich reward, hasten, then, and seize your arms, with the favor of the gods....

　　That most cruel and haughty nation considers everything its own, and at its own disposal; it thinks it right that it should regulate with whom we are to have war, with whom peace; it circumscribes and shuts us up by the boundaries of mountains and rivers which we must not pass, and then does not adhere to those boundaries which it appointed....They have sent the
20　two consuls of this year, one to Africa, the other to Spain: there is nothing left to us in any quarter, except what we can assert to ourselves by arms. Those may be cowards and dastards who have something to look back upon; whom, flying through safe and unmolested roads, their own lands and their own country will receive: there is a necessity for you to be brave, and, since all between **fruition** and death is broken off from you by inevitable despair, either
25　to conquer, or if fortune should waver, to meet death rather in battle than in flight. If this be well fixed and determined in the minds of you all, I will repeat, you have already conquered; no stronger incentive to victory has been given to man by the immortal gods.

Passage 2

Napoleon's Speech to his Soldiers:
At the Beginning of the Italian Campaign

Soldiers: You are naked and ill-fed! Government owes you much and can give you nothing.
The patience and courage you have shown in the midst of this **fallow** wilderness are admirable;
but they gain you no renown; no glory results to you from your endurance. It is my design
to lead you into the most fertile plains of the world. Rich provinces and great cities will be in
5   your power; there you will find honor, glory, and wealth. Soldiers of Italy, will you be wanting
in courage or perseverance?

Napoleon's Speech to his Soldiers: On Entering Milan

Soldiers: You have rushed like a torrent from the top of the Apennines; you have overthrown
and scattered all that opposed your march. Piedmont, delivered from Austrian tyranny,
indulges her natural sentiments of peace and friendship toward France. Milan is yours, and
10   the republican flag waves throughout Lombardy. The dukes of Parma and Modena owe their
political existence to your generosity alone.

The army which so proudly threatened you can find no barrier to protect it against your courage; neither the Po, the Ticino, nor the Adda could stop you for a single day. These vaunted
bulwarks of Italy opposed you in vain; you passed them as rapidly as the Apennines.

15   These great successes have filled the heart of your country with joy. Your representatives have
ordered a festival to commemorate your victories, which has been held in every district of the
republic. There your fathers, your mothers, your wives, sisters, and mistresses rejoiced in your
good fortune and proudly boasted of belonging to you.

Yes, soldiers, you have done much—but remains there nothing more to do? Shall it be said of
20   us that we knew how to conquer, but not how to make use of victory? Shall posterity reproach
us with having found Capua in Lombardy?

But I see you already hasten to arms. An effeminate repose is tedious to you; the days which are
lost to glory are lost to your happiness. Well, then, let us set forth!

1A. Which choice best describes the intent of lines 4-8 in passage 1?
   A.   to remind the soldiers of their own personal strength
   B.   to express the difficulty of crossing the Po River
   C.   to warn the soldiers about the Roman Navy
   D.   to emphasize that the soldiers cannot turn back
   E.   to contrast the Po and Rhone Rivers

1B. In lines 4-8, to whom does Hannibal compare his soldiers?
   A.   their fathers
   B.   gods
   C.   the enemy
   D.   war horses
   E.   prisoners

2A. As used in line 13 of the first passage, *recompense* most nearly means
   A.   restitution.
   B.   sacrifice.
   C.   expenditure.
   D.   revenge.
   E.   acceptance.

2B. Why, according to lines 9-15, is the *recompense* valuable beyond sentimental reasons?
   A.   The Carthaginians will reclaim their land.
   B.   The Romans are wealthy, successful conquerors.
   C.   The soldiers have the opportunity to recover what their fathers lost.
   D.   Hannibal's soldiers have already fought the Romans once.
   E.   Using the reward, Carthage can build a new fleet to escape.

3A. According to paragraph 3 of the first passage, why do the Romans deserve to be attacked?
   A.   Rome invaded Egypt and Portugal.
   B.   The Romans are "cowards and dastards" who deserve war.
   C.   The Romans took Sicily and Pisa from Carthage.
   D.   Rome is tyrannical and exploitative to the Carthaginians.
   E.   The Carthaginians are freezing in the Alps because the Romans have leveled all the forests around them.

3B. Choose the reason that best describes why Hannibal's enemy, according to him, will not be as brave as the Carthaginians.
   A.   Only Hannibal knows the true size of the Roman legions the soldiers will battle, and he will not reveal it to his own troops.
   B.   Hannibal's soldiers are fighting invaders in their homeland.
   C.   Soldiers do not fight bravely if they know they have a possible path of retreat.
   D.   Few of the Roman troops are veterans, unlike the seasoned Carthaginian forces.
   E.   The enemy's wealth and luxury has taken away its will to engage in battle.

4A. According to paragraph 1 of the second passage, what should motivate Napoleon's soldiers in battle?
   A.   the chance to win more territory for their government
   B.   the possibility to demonstrate perseverance in the face of difficulty
   C.   the prospect of individual renown and prosperity
   D.   the timeless virtues of delayed gratification and bravery
   E.   the opportunity to grow successful crops in Italy

4B. Napoleon devalues a few things in the first paragraph of his speech. Which choice identifies the action that will provide the soldiers with real rewards, according to Napoleon?
   A.   fulfilling one's duty
   B.   enduring a poorly supplied campaign
   C.   seizing the wealth of others
   D.   requesting government compensation
   E.   showing courage surviving the wilderness

5A. Napoleon probably uses the phrase, "as rapidly as the Apennines" in line 14 of the second passage to
   A.   highlight the difficulties the soldiers have faced so far.
   B.   emphasize the deliberate pace of the expedition.
   C.   express the speed and power of the French invasion.
   D.   relieve the soldiers' worries about invading Milan.
   E.   downplay the seriousness of previous casualties.

5B. Which choice best describes Napoleon's intent in lines 7-11?
   A.   He is describing his army's agenda for the invasion.
   B.   He is warning the soldiers of events yet to come.
   C.   He is trying to intimidate the enemy.
   D.   He is explaining the French's political connection to Austria.
   E.   He is instilling confidence by listing the army's successes.

6A. As used in line 14 of the second passage, *bulwarks* most nearly means
   A.   armies.
   B.   landmarks.
   C.   hills.
   D.   hallmarks.
   E.   defenses.

6B. Napoleon describes the bulwarks as *vaunted,* amid a list of his own army's achievements. *Vaunted* probably means
   A.   condemned.
   B.   poorly trained.
   C.   allied.
   D.   boasted of.
   E.   swiftly mobile.

7A. The tone of passage 1, as it compares to the tone of passage 2, can best be described as
   A.   didactic.
   B.   restrained.
   C.   effusive.
   D.   cynical.
   E.   sentimental.

7B. What does Napoleon include in his speech which Hannibal omits?
   A.   specific past victories
   B.   details of the troops' suffering
   C.   mention of treasure to be taken
   D.   his own force's superiority over the enemy
   E.   approval of what the troops have already accomplished

8A. The authors of both passages have different perspectives of fate. Which of the following identifies the difference?
   A.   Only Hannibal downplays the role of government in the future of the war.
   B.   Only Napoleon asks the soldiers to be courageous in the face of adversity.
   C.   Only Hannibal acknowledges divine intervention as a factor in the war.
   D.   Only Napoleon's soldiers are motivated by personal glory and wealth.
   E.   Only Napoleon points out the difficulties of the battle ahead.

8B. Which choice is an important part of battle for both Hannibal and Napoleon?
   A.   medals
   B.   family
   C.   glory
   D.   religion
   E.   recognition at home

9A. Which of the following identifies a similarity between the two passages?
   A.   Both generals are addressing their soldiers after a battle.
   B.   Both armies are invading foreign lands.
   C.   Both Napoleon and Hannibal appeal to God for intervention.
   D.   Both generals point out the shortcomings of their respective governments.
   E.   Both generals warn their soldiers about complacency in battle.

9B. What landmark do both Hannibal and Napoleon specifically mention?
   A.   the republic
   B.   Milan
   C.   Piedmont
   D.   Lombardy
   E.   The River Po

10A. Which of the following is a motivational factor for the Carthaginians, but not for Napoleon's soldiers?
   A.   The Carthaginian government has no way to compensate its soldiers.
   B.   The Carthaginians are fighting to regain their sovereignty.
   C.   The Carthaginians are better at surviving in the wilderness.
   D.   The Carthaginians must cross the treacherous Po River.
   E.   The Carthaginians fight to conquer; the French fight out of necessity.

10B. The most accurate description of Hannibal's motive can be described as
   A.   revenge.
   B.   conquest.
   C.   usurpation.
   D.   glory.
   E.   expansion.

Lesson Five

1. **ingrate**   (in´ grāt)   *n.*   a person who offers no thanks
    The mechanic fixed the weary traveler's car for free, and the *ingrate* left town without so much as a "thank you."

2. **status quo**   (sta´ təs kwō)   *n.*   the existing situation or state of affairs
    The mayoral candidate accused the current mayor of not trying to change the *status quo*, even though people are suffering and easy solutions are available.

3. **jeopardize**   (je´ pûr dīz)   *v.*   to put in danger
    Unnecessary use of the radio will *jeopardize* the secret mission because the enemy might hear the transmission.
    syn: endanger; imperil   *ant: defend; protect*

4. **waylay**   (wā´ lā)   *v.*   to interrupt or attack unexpectedly
    Dave sneaks out the back door sometimes because his nosy neighbor always *waylays* him and wants to talk for hours.
    syn: ambush; bushwhack

5. **intervene**   (in tər vēn´)   *v.*   to interfere with events, usually to improve
        the outcome
    The teachers will *intervene* if the students' argument gets out of control.
    syn: intercede; mediate   *ant: ignore; overlook*

6. **jaded**   (jā´ dəd)   *adj.*   worn out; dulled, as from overindulgence
    Kate became *jaded* about love after the third boyfriend in a month broke up with her.
    syn: exhausted; wearied   *ant: fresh*

7. **gist**   (jist)   *n.*   the main point
    I never did understand the *gist* of his story.
    syn: idea; essence

8. **advocate**   (ad´ və kāt)   *v.*   to recommend; to speak in favor of
    The organization is neutral and does not *advocate* support of a particular candidate or position.
    syn: promote; encourage   *ant: oppose; contest*

9. **efface**   (i fās´, e)   *v.*   to obliterate; to wipe out
    He tried to *efface* his memories of her by burning all her pictures.
    syn: erase   *ant: enshrine*

10. **charisma** (kə riz´ mə) *n.* personal appeal or attraction; magnetism
The candidate had *charisma* and good looks, but little knowledge of important issues.
syn: charm

11. **ogre** (ō´ gər) *n.* a brute; a large monster; a frightful giant
The *ogre* in the fairy tale occasionally emerges from his mountain cave and terrorizes the villagers.

12. **mesmerize** (mez´ mə rīz) *v.* to hypnotize
The fast music and spinning dancers *mesmerized* the audience.
syn: captivate; entrance　　　　　　　　　*ant: bore*

13. **entity** (en´ ti tē) *n.* anything having existence, either physical or mystical
Ann thought that she saw a ghostly *entity* hovering over the graveyard, but it turned out to be a flag.

14. **bandy** (ban´ dē) *v.* to exchange words; to discuss casually
Let's not *bandy* words about the deal any more; just sign the papers and leave, please.

15. **dastardly** (das´ tərd lē) *adj.* cowardly and treacherous
The *dastardly* thief stole money only from helpless, elderly people.
syn: dishonorable; shameful　　　　　　　*ant: righteous*

Lesson Five

Exercise I

Words in Context

From the list below, supply the words needed to complete the paragraph. Some words will not be used.

charisma   efface   advocate   mesmerize
gist   bandy   ogre

1. Joan, who _advocated_ the cleanup of the James River, is always trying to gain supporters for her cause. The usual _gist_ of her speech focuses on the effects of the river's pollution on future generations. Her eloquent speech _mesmerized_ audiences, and her _charism_ helps her to win the hearts of people who are not even affected by the pollution. Joan hopes someday to _efface_ the consequences of the irresponsible dumping practices that continue to foul the James River.

From the list below, supply the words needed to complete the paragraph. Some words will not be used.

dastardly   gist   entity   jaded
ogre   bandy   charisma

2. The _____ athlete, accustomed to winning first place, wanted to be happy with her third-place trophy, but deep down, she felt that months of intensive training had gone to waste. On the bus ride home, she refused to _____ compliments or even joke about the race with her teammates. She could think only about the _____ runner who intentionally tripped her early in the race and likely cost her the win. Myra could not believe that such an unsportsmanlike _ogre_ was allowed to compete in track meets.

From the list below, supply the words needed to complete the paragraph. Some words will not be used.

intervene   jeopardize   efface   bandy
ingrate   waylay   status quo

3. When a family emergency _____ Brian's college education, he feared that he would be considered a[n] _____ for refusing the substantial scholarship he had won, and that it would _____ his future chances of winning the award. To his surprise, the members of the board were impressed that he had chosen to rise above the _____ and forego school in order to take care of his ailing father; the board president even promised to _____ if anyone questioned Brian's scholarship while he put college on hold.

Exercise II

Sentence Completion

Complete the sentence in a way that shows you understand the meaning of the italicized vocabulary word.

1. Sally described enough of the movie for Bill to get the *gist* of it, but not enough to...

2. The jury was shocked when, during the trial, the *dastardly* criminal...

3. Mom would not *bandy* any words with me about extending my curfew because she felt that...

4. The *jaded* artist decided to find a new career when...

5. The revolutionaries *effaced* statues of the former dictator because...

6. Mondello the Great *mesmerized* the children at the birthday party by...

7. Someone who *advocates* good manners might become angry if you...

8. The overwhelming *charisma* of the cult leader made it easy for him to...

9. The linebackers on the football team looked like *ogres* compared to...

10. Mom had to explain to Maggie that an imaginary friend is not a real *entity*; it is...

11. You will be considered an *ingrate* if you...

12. Writers who break from the *status quo* can...

13. One thing that can *jeopardize* your grades is...

14. The persistent vendors *waylay* anyone who...

15. Steve dropped his lunch and *intervened* when...

Exercise III

Roots, Prefixes, and Suffixes

Study the entries and answer the questions that follow.

The root *fort* means "strong."
The root *graph* means "writing."
The root *gen* means "born," "to produce," or "kind" (type).
The prefix *mono–* means "one."

1. Using *literal* translations as guidance, define the following words without using a dictionary.

    A. generic   D. fort
    B. generate   E. monologue
    C. fortify   F. graphic

2. The coach says that this year, the strong players on the team have the _____ to make it to the championships. The activity that you do best—your strong point— might be called your _____.

3. A group of people born within a certain time period is a[n] _____. Your _____ will determine what physical traits you have.

4. List all the words you can think of that contain the root *graph* or *gen*.

Exercise IV

Inference

Complete the sentence by inferring information about the italicized word from its context.

1. If you didn't understand the *gist* of the lecture, then you should find the teacher after class and ask...

2. When someone who *advocates* energy conservation sees lights left on, he or she might...

3. If you *efface* your fears about flying, then you might be willing to...

Exercise V

Writing

Here is a writing prompt similar to the one you will find on the writing portion of an assessment test.

Plan and write an essay based on the following statement:

> The Kites of olden times, as well as the Swans, had the privilege of song. But having heard the neigh of the horse, they were so enchanted with the sound, that they tried to imitate it; and, in trying to neigh, they forgot how to sing.
>
> –Aesop, Sixth Century B.C.

Assignment: Aesop was a prolific fabulist who used animals in his fables. In an essay, explain why Aesop used kites (hawks) and swans to convey the moral lesson of his fable, and then provide a modern explanation of the message. Include your own opinion of the lesson, and support your idea with evidence from your reading, classroom studies, experience, and observation.

Thesis: Write a *one-sentence* response to the assignment. Make certain this single sentence offers a clear statement of your position.

Example: In his fable about kites and swans, Aesop is attempting to impart the message that people who automatically follow trends or try to emulate others risk losing their own identities.

_____

_____

Organizational Plan: List at least three subtopics you will use to support your main idea. This list is your outline.

1. _____

2. _____

3. _____

Draft: Following your outline, write a good first draft of your essay. Remember to support all your points with examples, facts, references to reading, etc.

Review and Revise: Exchange essays with a classmate. Using the scoring guide for Sentence Formation and Variety on page 254, score your partner's essay (while he or she scores yours). Focus on sentence structure and the use of language conventions. If necessary, rewrite your essay to improve the sentence structure and/or your use of language.

Exercise VI

English Practice

Identifying Sentence Errors

Identify the grammatical error in each of the following sentences. If the sentence contains no error, select answer choice E.

1. Larry <u>said that he</u> had personally <u>designed</u> the web pages with the <u>help of himself</u>
          (A)   (B)   (C)

    and <u>his employees</u>.   No error
          (D)   (E)

2. <u>I didn't</u> do <u>nothing for the last ten</u> minutes <u>but argue</u>
      (A)   (B)   (C)

    <u>with my sister.</u>   No error
       (D)   (E)

3. <u>Problems with</u> aggressive <u>wildlife often begins</u> <u>with aggressive human</u>
        (A)   (B)   (C)

    <u>beings.</u>   No error
     (D)   (E)

4. <u>Hot and full of sick people,</u> the patients <u>in the front room</u> <u>were given</u>
            (A)   (B)   (C)

    their <u>flu shots</u>.   No error
       (D)   (E)

5. Proponents <u>for the construction</u> of a new intrastate expressway <u>includes</u>
           (A)   (B)

    at least four <u>people</u> known <u>to be affiliated</u> with organized
            (C)   (D)

    crime operations.   No error
             (E)

Improving Sentences

The underlined portion of each sentence below contains some flaw. Select the answer choice that best corrects the flaw.

6. <u>The victims were lying on the ground and firemen arrived to douse the flames and take them to the hospital.</u>
    A. The victims were lying on the ground when firemen arrived to douse the flames and take them to the hospital.
    B. Fireman arrived to douse the flames and to take the victims lying on the ground to the hospital.
    C. After dousing the flames on the ground, the firemen took the victims to the hospital.
    D. Firemen arrived to douse the flames, when victims were lying on the ground, and they were taken to the hospital.
    E. Victims lying on the ground were taken to the hospital and firemen arrived to douse the flames.

7. Because of the hurricane warning, everyone <u>sat inside and talked about the game around the dining room table.</u>
    A. sat inside around the dining room table and talked about the game.
    B. sat inside the game and talked around the dining room table.
    C. sat inside the dining room and talked about the table.
    D. sat and talked inside the game around the table in the dining room.
    E. talked about the game and sat at the dining room table.

8. We intend to measure the individual results <u>against its costs.</u>
    A. against the costs.
    B. against costs.
    C. against their costs.
    D. with their costs.
    E. against the individual costs.

9. Deep-sea fishing no longer fascinates me as much as <u>to go to computer demonstrations.</u>
    A. I am interested in computer demonstrations.
    B. going to computer demonstrations.
    C. to go to a computer demonstration.
    D. computer demonstrations.
    E. demonstrating computers.

10. <u>Amadeus Mozart was a brilliant composer he was said to be a little crazy.</u>
    A. Amadeus Mozart was said to be a little crazy, he was a brilliant composer.
    B. A brilliant composer Amadeus Mozart was. He was also said to be a little crazy.
    C. Although a brilliant composer, Amadeus Mozart was said to be a little crazy.
    D. He was said to be a little crazy, Amadeus Mozart was a brilliant composer.
    E. A brilliant composer, although a little crazy, was said to be Amadeus Mozart.

Lesson Six

1. **indisposed** (in di spozd´) *adj.* slightly ill
Taylor was *indisposed* all week, so her teacher allowed her to email her assignments from home so she wouldn't fall behind.
syn: ailing; peaked   *ant: healthy; well*

2. **stark** (stärk) *adj.* grim and barren
Days after the atomic weapon test, the blast area had become a *stark* field of smoking gravel, devoid of any life.
syn: bleak; austere   *ant: vibrant*

3. **commandeer** (käw mən dēr´) *v.* to seize property for official use
Detective Hammer *commandeered* a citizen's car and mashed the throttle, speeding off in pursuit of the fleeing serial killer.
syn: capture; appropriate

4. **sally** (sa´ lē) *v.* to rush forward suddenly, usually from a defensive position
The dictator's generals ordered the front-line troops to *sally* forth and attack the enemy or be shot for treason.
syn: charge

5. **cadence** (kā´ dens) *n.* the rhythmic flow of an activity, especially marching or dancing
After a mile into the marathon, Kira found a comfortable *cadence* that would get her through the next 25 miles.
syn: beat; meter

6. **nepotism** (nep´ ə tiz əm) *n.* favoritism shown to family or friends by those in power, especially in business or hiring practices
I was qualified for the job, but Uncle Mike refused to hire me because he did not want to be accused of *nepotism*.

7. **begrudge** (bi gruj´) *v.* to resent another's success; to envy
Craig, the younger brother, secretly *begrudged* Brian's fortune.
syn: resent   *ant: forgive*

8. **mandarin** (man´ də rin) *n.* an influential person; a member of an elite group
Mandarins and bureaucrats discussed the state of the economy during the summit.

9. **glutinous** (glōō′ tə nəs) *adj.* gluey; sticky
The bread dough was in a *glutinous* mass that stuck to anything it touched.

10. **enmity** (en′ mi tē) *n.* deep-seated hostility, often mutual
Angry stares revealed the mutual *enmity* between Steve and his supervisor.
syn: hatred; antagonism   *ant: friendship*

11. **declaim** (di klām′) *v.* to speak in a dramatic, impassioned,
          or blustering manner
At the debate, each politician *declaimed* against the policies of the others.
syn: trumpet   *ant: whisper*

12. **imbue** (im byōō′) *v.* to inspire or influence; to saturate
Her hard-working mother *imbued* Jane with a solid work ethic.
syn: instill; pervade

13. **gaffe** (gaf) *n.* an embarrassing public mistake or remark
The applicant forgot the name of the company during his job interview, and his *gaffe* cost him the position.
syn: blunder; faux pas

14. **quaff** (kwof) *v.* to drink in large quantities; to gulp
The old captain *quaffed* his ale and then ordered another pint.
syn: guzzle; swig   *ant: sip*

15. **bibliophile** (bib′ lē ə fīl) *n.* a lover of books
The *bibliophile* was thrilled to get a job at the library.

Exercise I

Words in Context

From the list below, supply the words needed to complete the paragraph. Some words will not be used.

nepotism	declaim	imbue	enmity
begrudge	cadence		

1. The _enmity_ between Mike and Brad showed in the way they argued over the most trivial company decisions. Weeks before, Brad had been promoted to regional manager in an obvious act of _nepotism,_ since his uncle is a member of the board of directors. Mike _begrudged_ Brad for the promotion because it had taken fifteen years for Mike to become a regional manager, and Brad had walked into the job with almost no experience at all. Now, during any argument with Brad, Mike was sure to _declaim_ about how "fifteen years of seniority and experience make my decisions virtually infallible."

From the list below, supply the words needed to complete the paragraph. Some words will not be used.

nepotism	mandarin	imbue	bibliophile
commandeer			

2. Corporate leaders, high-ranking government officials, and influential _mandarins_ gathered in the halls of Xavier's mansion at least once a month. Dinner was held in the ballroom, and then Xavier, a noted _bibliophile,_ usually invited his guests to his colossal private library. Bookshelves towered over the guests, and the presence of hundreds of rare, ancient tomes _imbued_ them with a sense of humility as they stood among the centuries of human thought that had built the world in which they now lived.

From the list below, supply the words needed to complete the paragraph. Some words will not be used.

glutinous	quaff	declaim	gaffe
indisposed			

3. As a food critic, Veronica was paid to _declaim_ about her latest discoveries in the restaurant scene, but demand for her column dwindled after her latest _gaffe_, in which she mistakenly _quaffed_ the lemon juice left in a finger bowl on her table, unaware that the liquid was, in fact, intended for cleaning her hands.

From the list below, supply the words needed to complete the paragraph. Some words will not be used.

indisposed   imbue   sally   commandeer

declaim   cadence   stark *adj*

4. The inmate had planned his escape for years while enduring the _stark_ conditions of the castle dungeon in which his brother, the false king, had confined him. First, he would slip tainted meat into the guard's meal, which would render him _indisposed_ for a while. When he could no longer hear the _cadence_ of the patrolling guards' footsteps, he would flee to the courtyard and _commandeer_ a horse. Once quietly passing through the open gates, the inmate would leave the road and _sally_ through the thickest part of the forest in order to make it difficult for his pursuers to track him.

Exercise II

Sentence Completion

Complete the sentence in a way that shows you understand the meaning of the italicized vocabulary word.

1. During a break from toiling in the oppressive heat, the workers *quaffed*... the beer.
2. Dad spent all day fixing the car and then *declaimed* that... I had broken it.
3. While making first contact with the isolated tribe, the explorers feared that the smallest *gaffe* could... get them killed.
4. Some parents accused the coach of *nepotism* because... his kid was a started.
5. Working on a farm *imbued* Mary with... a good work ethic
6. The activists wanted Dorian's support because he is a *mandarin* who can... give good advice
7. You knew that Frank was a *bibliophile* because... he had read 100s of books.
8. The scientist said that the *glutinous* substance had similar characteristics to... slime
9. There was *enmity* between the brother and sister ever since.. she stole his company.
10. Gloria secretly *begrudged* her friend... bcs she won the cheer comp.
11. Because she was *indisposed* on Saturday, Ophelia could not... go to church.
12. The family had lived a *stark* existence ever since... their son passed.
13. During the first phase of the invasion, troops *commandeered*... the peasants' houses.
14. If we don't *sally* forward on this project, then... you won't get it done.
15. To ensure that everyone marched at the same *cadence*, the drum major... set the tempo.

Exercise III

Roots, Prefixes, and Suffixes

Study the entries and answer the questions that follow.

The prefix *biblio–* means "book."
The root *mort* means "death."
The roots *voc* and *vok* mean "to call."

1. Using *literal* translations as guidance, define the following words without using a dictionary.

    A. bibliography   D. vocation
    B. biblical   E. vociferous
    C. mortician   F. mortuary

2. If you get too many speeding tickets, the department of transportation might call back, or _____, your driver's license. An *advocate* is someone who _____ a particular cause.

3. List as many words as you can think of that contain the root, *mort, voc,* or *vok*.

Exercise IV

Inference

Complete the sentence by inferring information about the italicized word from its context.

1. *Nepotism* is common in family businesses, where many of the employees are hired because they…

2. Kelly attributed her artistic success to the fact that her mentor had *imbued* her with…

3. If people avoid you because you always *declaim* your own skills, then you should probably learn to…

Exercise V

Critical Reading

Below is a reading passage followed by several multiple-choice questions. Carefully read the passage and choose the best answer for each of the questions.

The following passage is an adaptation of a letter written in 1904 by President Theodore Roosevelt. Roosevelt is remembered for his limitless energy, his aggressive foreign and domestic policies, his economic reform, and his often-militant patriotic fervor. The passage reveals a side of Roosevelt of which many citizens were unaware.

Dear Ted:

This will be a long business letter. I sent to you the examination papers for West Point and Annapolis. I have thought a great deal over the matter, and discussed it at great length with Mother. I feel on the one hand that I ought to give you my best advice, and yet on the other hand I do not wish to seem to **commandeer** your wishes. If you have definitely made
5   up your mind that you have an overmastering desire to be in the Navy or the Army, and that such a career is the one in which you will take a really heart-felt interest—far more so than any other—and that your greatest chance for happiness and usefulness will lie in doing this one work to which you feel yourself especially drawn—why, under such circumstances, I have but little to say. But I am not satisfied that this is really your feeling. It seemed to me more as if you
10   did not feel drawn in any other direction, and wondered what you were going to do in life or what kind of work you would turn your hand to, and wondered if you could make a success or not; and that you are therefore inclined to turn to the Navy or Army chiefly because you would then have a definite and settled career in life, and could hope to go on steadily without any great risk of failure. Now, if such is your thought, I shall quote to you what Captain Mahan
15   said of his son when asked why he did not send him to West Point or Annapolis. "I have too much confidence in him to make me feel that it is desirable for him to enter either branch of the service."

I have great confidence in you. I believe you have the ability and, above all, the energy, the perseverance, and the common sense, to win out in civil life. That you will have some hard
20   times and some discouraging times I have no question; but this is merely another way of saying that you will share the common lot. Though you will have to work in different ways from those in which I worked, you will not have to work any harder, nor to face periods of more discouragement. I trust in your ability, and especially your character, and I am confident you will **sally** ahead to success.
25   In the Army and the Navy the chance for a man to show great ability and rise above his fellows does not occur on the average more than once in a generation. When I was down at Santiago it was melancholy for me to see how fossilized and lacking in ambition, and generally useless, were most of the men of my age and over, who had served their lives in the Army. The Navy for the last few years has been better, but for twenty years after the Civil War there
30   was less chance in the Navy than in the Army to practice, and do, work of real consequence. I have actually known lieutenants in both the Army and the Navy who were grandfathers—men who had seen their children married before they themselves attained the grade of captain. Of course the chance may come at any time when the man of West Point or Annapolis who will have stayed in the Army or Navy finds a great war on, and therefore has the opportunity to
35   rise high. Under such circumstances, I think that the man of such training who has actually left the Army or the Navy has even more chance of rising than the man who has remained in it. Moreover, often a man can do as I did in the Spanish War, even though not a West-Pointer. This last point raises the question about you going to West Point or Annapolis and leaving the Army or Navy after you have served the regulation four years (I think that is the number) after

40 graduation from the academy. Under this plan you would have an excellent education and a grounding in discipline and, in some ways, a testing of your capacity greater than I think you can get in any ordinary college. On the other hand, except for the profession of an engineer, you would have had nothing like special training, and you would be so ordered about, and arranged for, that you would have less independence of character than you could gain from

45 them. You would have had fewer temptations; but you would have had less chance to develop the qualities which overcome temptations and show that a man has individual initiative. Supposing you entered at seventeen, with the intention of following this course. The result would be that at twenty-five you would leave the Army or Navy without having gone through any law school or any special technical school of any kind, and would start your life work three

50 or four years later than your schoolfellows of today, who go to work immediately after leaving college. Of course, under such circumstances, you might study law, for instance, during the four years after graduation; but my own feeling is that a man does good work chiefly when he is in something which he intends to make his permanent work, and in which he is deeply interested. Moreover, there will always be the chance that the number of officers in the Army

55 or Navy will be deficient, and that you would have to stay in the service instead of getting out when you wished.

I want you to think over all these matters very seriously. It would be a great misfortune for you to start into the Army or Navy as a career, and find that you had mistaken your desires and had gone in without really weighing the matter. You ought not to enter unless the life

60 genuinely **imbues** you as a life-work. If so, go in; but not otherwise.

Mr. Loeb told me today that at seventeen he had tried for the army, but failed. The competitor who beat him in is now a captain; Mr. Loeb has passed him by, although meanwhile a war has been fought. Mr. Loeb says he wished to enter the army because he did not know what to do, could not foresee whether he would succeed or fail in life, and felt the army would

65 give him "a living and a career." Now if this is at bottom your feeling I should advise you not to go in; I should say yes to some boys, but not to you; I believe in you too much, and have too much confidence in you.

1A. The passage is a letter from a[n]
   A.   brother to a brother.
   B.   uncle to a nephew.
   C.   father to a son.
   D.   teacher to a student.
   E.   president to a secretary.

1B. The tone of the letter is best described as
   A.   celebrative.
   B.   concern.
   C.   admonishment.
   D.   critical.
   E.   irritated.

2A. Which of the following best describes the purpose of the passage?
   A.   describe
   B.   entertain
   C.   analyze
   D.   persuade
   E.   inform

2B. Which line from the passage best identifies and supports Roosevelt's motive for writing the letter?
    A. "I sent to you the examination papers for West Point and Annapolis."
    B. "That you will have some hard times and some discouraging times I have no question..."
    C. "But I am not satisfied that this is really your feeling."
    D. "I trust in your ability, and especially your character, and I am confident you will sally ahead to success."
    E. "I have great confidence in you."

3A. According to the author, Ted wants to attend military school because
    A. he knows that the military will provide opportunities for success.
    B. he doesn't know what he wants to do, but he wants a steady career.
    C. he wants a steady career that offers more excitement than college does.
    D. his father was a war hero who became president.
    E. Captain Mahan told Ted that he would have potential as an officer.

3B. What kind of real evidence does the author provide for his argument against Ted's military career?
    A. stories the author read about the Navy
    B. his own observations from military experience
    C. predictions of Ted's probable uneventful career path
    D. rumors of military cutbacks based on his knowledge of government
    E. the differences between business and military careers

4A. According to the author of the passage, participating in a war is
    A. detrimental, because of the risk.
    B. an opportunity to succeed.
    C. character-building because it provides better challenges than college does.
    D. good for professional soldiers, but not sailors.
    E. not a good idea for people who want to be promoted.

4B. The negative side to the answer to question 4A, according to the author, is
    A. the psychological trauma.
    B. the disparity between military rank and civilian career status.
    C. the frequency of duty.
    D. the unprofessional colleagues who get promoted first.
    E. the rarity of the event.

5A. Which choice is *not* a reason why a military education followed by a short tour of duty would be beneficial?
    A. The military helps to develop discipline.
    B. Military schools provide excellent educations.
    C. The military would prepare a student for a political career.
    D. A military engineer would have the special training for a civilian career.
    E. The military would provide challenges unavailable to civilians.

5B. Choose the term that best describes the author's argumentative strategy, which is made apparent in question 5A.
   A. counterarguments to Ted's military ambitions
   B. arguments both for and against Ted's military plans
   C. arguments in support of Ted's military service
   D. arguments against Ted's judgment
   E. logic based only on the author's military experience

6A. Which best paraphrases the following quotation? (lines 52-54)

> "...my own feeling is that a man does good work chiefly when he is in something which he intends to make his permanent work, and in which he is deeply interested."

   A. People who do not choose the right career just have to learn to deal with it.
   B. Decide what you want to do before committing your life to a career.
   C. Choose your career based on what you want to do for the rest of your life.
   D. People do their best work when they love what they are doing.
   E. Choosing a career path should depend on how much ambition you have.

6B. The answer to question 6A suggests that Roosevelt places substantial value in
   A. always working hard, no matter what one thinks of the job.
   B. recognition for merit while on the job.
   C. equal wages.
   D. personal satisfaction with one's career.
   E. the adaptability to be happy in any career.

7A. As used in line 55, *deficient* most nearly means
   A. lacking.
   B. deployed.
   C. captured.
   D. defective.
   E. improper.

7B. Choose the line from the passage that supports your answer to question 7A.
   A. "...my own feeling is that a man does good work..."
   B. "...you would have to stay in the service instead of getting out when you wished."
   C. "...you might study law, for instance, during the four years after graduation."
   D. "...at twenty-five you would leave the Army or Navy without having gone through any law school or any special technical school..."
   E. "...gone in without really weighing the matter."

8A. According to the passage, the existence of temptation is
    A. dangerous because it can lead to imprisonment in the military.
    B. good because it provokes thought.
    C. not covered in the letter.
    D. necessary because it separates the good from the bad.
    E. good because it inspires resistance and individuality.

8B. The author claims that temptation is greatest in
    A. law school.
    B. the Navy.
    C. the Spanish War.
    D. the civilian world.
    E. military academies.

9A. Mr. Loeb was Roosevelt's advisor. The mention of Loeb's story in the final paragraph suggests which of the following?
    A. People can achieve as much success as civilians as they can as members of the military.
    B. Loeb was lucky to become a presidential advisor.
    C. People should enlist in the Navy, not the Army.
    D. People who do not make Captain should leave the Army because they can get better civilian careers.
    E. People who lack confidence will not succeed in the military.

9B. The story of Mr. Loeb, in the final paragraph, is included to be an analogy of
    A. people who should have joined the military.
    B. Roosevelt, the author.
    C. a student who first chose college over the military.
    D. the competitor who made Captain.
    E. Ted, the recipient of the letter.

10A. The author's tone is best described as
    A. anxious and judgmental.
    B. panicked and bossy.
    C. advisory and supportive.
    D. serious and demanding.
    E. pleased and affectionate.

10B. Which line from the text best supports your answer to question 10A?
    A. "I believe in you too much, and have too much confidence in you."
    B. "Moreover, often a man can do as I did in the Spanish War, even though not a West-Pointer."
    C. "That you will have some hard times and some discouraging times I have no question."
    D. "But I am not satisfied that this is really your feeling."
    E. "You would have had fewer temptations; but you would have had less chance to develop the qualities which overcome temptations and show that a man has individual initiative."

Review Lessons 4-6

Exercise I

Inferences

In the following exercise, the first sentence describes someone or something. Infer information from the first sentence, and then choose the word from the Word Bank that best completes the second sentence.

denizen	ingrate	blight	nepotism
jeopardize	fallow	charisma	mesmerize

1. The candidates for the new management position were let down when the owner's son was given the job, in spite of his having no actual experience in that line of work.

    From this sentence, we can infer the company's owner practices _____.

2. Billions of grasshoppers descended upon the wheat fields, eating everything in sight and leaving miles of dusty stubble.

    From this sentence, we can infer that the insects were a[n] _____ upon the farmers.

3. The farmer planted the same crops year after year until the soil's nutrients had been used up, so he let the fields go unplanted for a few years until he found a good source of fertilizer.

    From this sentence, we can infer that the farmer allowed the fields to sit _____ for a while.

4. The train hauls several tanks of poisonous chemicals past the elementary school each day, and often the engineer exceeds the speed limit.

    From this sentence, we can infer the engineer's hazardous behavior _____ anyone near the railroad tracks.

5. The politician was equally loved and hated for his ideas, but even his greatest rivals warmed up to him within seconds of engaging him in conversation.

    From this sentence, we can infer that the politician has _____ that helps him get along with people.

Exercise II

Related Words

Some of the vocabulary words from Lessons 4 through 6 have related meanings. Complete the following sentences by choosing the word that best fits the context, based on information you infer from the use of the italicized word. Some word pairs will be antonyms, some will be synonyms, and some will simply be words often used in the same context.

1. The drill sergeant ordered the _____ to *sally* ahead and catch up to the rest of the platoon, or else they could look forward to scrubbing the latrine after the run.
   A. denizens
   B. bibliophiles
   C. laggards
   D. entities
   E. ruffians

2. The terrorist's *dastardly* plot to crash two oil tankers off the shore would _____ all the fishing, ecology, and tourism revenue on the Gulf Coast.
   A. enshroud
   B. intervene
   C. transcribe
   D. jeopardize
   E. declaim

3. Through his political connections and strategic bribes, Si had become a *mandarin* who was known to provide good jobs and business deals to those who demonstrated _____ to him.
   A. fealty
   B. gist
   C. enmity
   D. status quo
   E. paucity

4. Jack is a[n] _____, so it is pointless to try to *gratify* him because he will be neither pleased nor appreciative.
   A. charisma
   B. laggard
   C. ingrate
   D. bibliophile
   E. caricature

5. After his successful *gambit* to sail a glider out of the enemy prison camp, the prisoner _____ an unattended truck and drove straight for the border.
   A. mesmerized
   B. commandeered
   C. broached
   D. begrudged
   E. intervened

6. An irate customer *declaimed* her experience on numerous Internet blogs and review sites, and the restaurant spent months trying to _____ the comments before they scared any remaining customers away.
   A. efface
   B. accentuate
   C. imbue
   D. jeopardize
   E. gratify

7. Half the town *advocates* changing the law, causing an increase in taxes, while the other half wants to maintain the _____, claiming that something that isn't broken doesn't need to be fixed.
   A. fallow
   B. charisma
   C. epigram
   D. obsequy
   E. status quo

8. A *blight* descended upon the crops and turned the wheat black with fungus, leaving nothing in the distance except _____ fields that would not provide food for the winter.
   A. navigable
   B. licentious
   C. indisposed
   D. composite
   E. stark

9. The burglar *mesmerized* the guard dog by waving a juicy T-bone steak in its direction, and then he _____ the hungry animal into a closet and slammed the door shut.
   A. transcribed
   B. enticed
   C. imbued
   D. eluded
   E. mauled

10. Kristen did not *begrudge* people who were lucky enough to be born wealthy, but seeing them get jobs that she was more qualified to do caused her to become _____.
    A. jaded
    B. elated
    C. glutinous
    D. composite
    E. indisposed

Exercise III

Deeper Meanings

Choose a word to replace the italicized word in each sentence. All of the possible choices for each sentence have similar definitions, but the correct answer will have a connotation that best suits the context. For example, the words "delete," "destroy," and "obliterate" all mean "to remove or wipe out," but no one would ever say, "I destroyed the name from the document." The correct choice will be the word that has the best specific meaning and does not render the sentence awkward in tone or content. When choices seem close, look for a clue in the context that makes one choice better than the other.

Note that the correct answer is not always the primary vocabulary word from the lesson.

anger	move	intrudes	choice
gambit	bare	destruction	blight
enmity	stark	trouble	attacks
arrived			

1. Alex and Cassie become frustrated when Alex's uninvited brother *intervenes* during their recording sessions.

   Better word: _____

2. A deep *tension* between the brothers prevented them from talking to each other for several years.

   Better word: _____

3. The last of the soldiers knew that the escape plan was a dangerous *procedure* with a slim chance of success, but it was their only hope to survive.

   Better word: _____

4. After the large factory shut down, hundreds of families moved away in search of new work, leaving *plain* neighborhoods with empty streets, abandoned homes stripped of valuables, and eerie silence.

   Better word: _____

5. Repeated atomic tests caused a[n] *problem* on the tropical atoll, preventing any type of sea life from flourishing for many decades.

   Better word: _____

Exercise IV

Crossword Puzzle

Use the clues to complete the crossword puzzle. The answers consist of vocabulary words from Lessons 4 through 6.

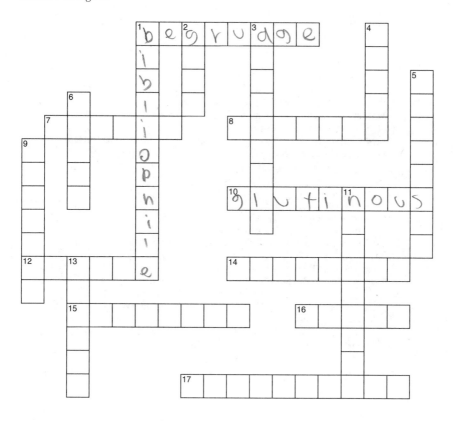

Across

1. hold against
7. risky strategy
8. slowpoke
10. like maple syrup
12. vandalize
14. helping out your kin
15. get behind
16. guzzle
17. legally steal

Down

1. bookworm
2. the truth of it
3. like a villain
4. tired of the routine
5. what makes a magnetic personality
6. big mistake
9. resident
11. passable
13. allegiance pledged

Exercise V

Subject Prompts

Here is a writing prompt similar to the one you will find on the writing portion of an assessment test. Follow the instructions below and write a brief, efficient essay.

> During World War II, many fences and store windows throughout the United States were spotted with posters that contained phrases such as "Loose lips sink ships." At the time, the largest military operation in the history of the planet was underway, and the United States was fighting on fronts in two hemispheres. In the meantime, the secrecy of the Manhattan Project—the plan to produce an atomic bomb—depended on thousands of people saying nothing in order to prevent the enemy from gaining an advantage or sabotaging the war effort.
>
> By definition, information classified as top secret, if released to the public, will cause grave danger to national security—imagine, for example, a terrorist group learning the top secret launch codes to a nuclear weapon. Not all secrets involve weapons, of course; sometimes, the classified data include intelligence collected about international trade, or weaknesses of allied nations. Lesser secrets are expected to be less damaging than top secret, but they are damaging nonetheless. Compromised secrets can shatter alliances, generate hostility, and weaken the nation's trade and commerce.
>
> The spread of Internet "whistleblower" sites on which anonymous government employees post classified information for the world to see has sparked debate between two perspectives of government: those who believe that secrets are necessary to a functioning nation, and those who believe that secrets merely enable tyranny and keep the population intentionally ignorant.
>
> Imagine that you have been appointed the Secretary of Defense, and that you have influence over the way in which classified information is managed. Take a side in the debate over classified information and address your opposition in a speech, explaining why you do or do not believe that secrets are important to the nation. Support your argument with at least three subtopics derived from your own experience, reading, observations, or reasoning.

Thesis: Write a *one-sentence* response to the above assignment. Make certain this single sentence offers a clear statement of your position.

Example: Secrets are paramount to a nation because as a sovereign country, we can trust only ourselves to look after our own interests.

_____

_____

Organizational Plan: List at least three subtopics you will use to support your main idea. This list is your outline.

1. _____

2. _____

3. _____

Draft: Following your outline, write a good first draft of your essay. Remember to support all your points with examples, facts, references to reading, etc.

Review and Revise: Exchange essays with a classmate. Using the scoring guide for Development on page 252, score your partner's essay (while he or she scores yours). Focus on the development of ideas and the use of language conventions. If necessary, rewrite your essay to incorporate more (or more relevant) support and/or improve your use of language.

primordial - primeval
term/stint - tenure
cover - laminate
confirm, verify, corroborate - substiate
brace - gird
intimidate - daunt
fluctuation, instability - flux
shanty, shack - hovel
ghastly - cadaverous
destitution - penury
passage - egress
exhiliration, vivacity - exuberance ☆
tyrant - despot

weath, opulance - penury
encourage - daunt
disprove, invalidate - substantiate
abuse, torture - dote
new, modern - primeval
palace, mansion - hovel
robust, healthy - cadaverous
ingress, entrance - egress
depressed, indifference - exuberante

Lesson Seven

1. **primeval** (prī mē′ vəl) *adj.* of the ancient, first ages of the world
   Earth's *primeval* oceans were filled with massive predatory fish that make the largest modern sharks look like harmless goldfish by comparison.
   syn: primordial; prehistoric   *ant: new; modern*

2. **dote** (dōt) *v.* to show excessive love for
   The queen *doted* on her adult son, the prince, causing subjects to secretly describe him as a "mommy's boy."
                                                     ant: abuse; torture

3. **tenure** (ten′ yər) *n.* the period of time a job lasts
   During your *tenure* as coach, you will be expected to attend every game of the season.
   syn: term; stint

4. **laminate** (la′ mə nāt) *v.* to make by bonding layers together
   The discount furniture company builds tables out of cheap plywood and then *laminates* them with thin layers of fancy wood.
   syn: cover

5. **substantiate** (sub stan′ chē āt) *v.* to support with proof or evidence
   A witness at the scene of the wreck *substantiated* the driver's excuse that a deer had run in front of her car.
   syn: confirm; verify; corroborate   *ant: disprove; invalidate*

6. **gird** (gûrd) *v.* to prepare for an event or an action
   Residents of the shore *girded* themselves for the upcoming hurricane.
   syn: brace

7. **daunt** (dônt) *v.* to make afraid; to discourage
   The high waves and the approaching storm did not *daunt* the treasure hunters.
   syn: intimidate; dishearten   *ant: encourage*

8. **flux** (fluks) *n.* a state of continual change or movement
   The high degree of *flux* in the stock market makes investing risky.
   syn: fluctuation; instability   *ant: stability; solidity*

9. **hovel** (hov′ əl) *n.* a wretched living place; an open shed
   The child welfare agency removed the children from the filthy *hovel*.
   syn: shanty; shack   *ant: palace; mansion*

10. **cadaverous** (kə dav′ r əs) *adj.* of or like a corpse; pale; gaunt; thin
The old pirate's *cadaverous* face made the young sailor tremble.
syn: ghastly   *ant: robust; healthy*

11. **gothic** (goth′ ik) *adj.* of the middle ages; of or relating to a mysterious,
grotesque, and desolate style of fiction
A romantic story line offset some of the dreary and gloomy elements of the *gothic* novel.

12. **penury** (pen′ yə rē) *n.* extreme poverty
Though born into *penury*, he became one of the country's wealthiest entrepreneurs.
syn: destitution   *ant: wealth; opulence*

13. **egress** (ē′ gres) *n.* an exit; a means of going out
The only *egress* on the submarine was the main hatch on the tower.
syn: passage   *ant: ingress; entrance*

14. **exuberance** (ek zōō′ bə rəns) *n.* high spirits; happy enthusiasm
The *exuberance* that accompanied Rose's new financial wealth waned when she
received the bill for her taxes.
syn: exhilaration; vivacity   *ant: depression; indifference*

15. **despot** (des′ pət) *n.* a dictator with absolute power
During his rule, Stalin was a *despot* responsible for the death of millions of his own
people.
syn: tyrant

Exercise I

Words in Context

From the list below, supply the words needed to complete the paragraph. Some words will not be used.

flux ✗	~~hovel~~ ✗	~~despot~~	~~cadaverous~~
egress ✗	~~penury~~	gird ✗	

corpse

1. When the _despot_ assassinated the monarch and seized control of the government, the already poor nation sank into abject _penury_. The majority of citizens lived in poorly maintained _novels_ that would likely be condemned by the standards of most other nations. Starvation and epidemics turned what should have been healthy, young workers into _cadaverous_ zombies who hoped to have enough energy to scrounge for roots to feed their families. Citizens had only two means of _egress_ from the misery—through the demilitarized zone or across the border into China. Escape was a risky undertaking; if captured, refugees faced imprisonment or execution.

From the list below, supply the words needed to complete the paragraph. Some words will not be used.

prepare   → *continual*

~~penury~~	~~gird~~	~~flux~~ *change*	exuberance
~~daunt~~	gothic	~~hovel~~	*happy*

2. Despite their tremendous destructive power, tornadoes do not _daunt_ the Russell family; they have experienced too many storms even to care. The weather of the Midwest is in _flux_, and the family seldom allows adverse weather to detract from the _____ of their day-to-day lives. Their underground shelter might resemble a[n] _hovel_ dungeon, but for the Russells, it is a place to sit out the storm and listen to Mr. Russell's stories about how he weathered tornadoes during his childhood. He often relates the day in which a tornado passed while he was far from shelter, and how he and his parents _gird_ themselves for the oncoming storm.

From the list below, supply the words needed to complete the paragraph. Some words will not be used.

primeval	exuberance	dote	tenure
laminate	hovel	substantiate	

→ *proof*

3. During Dr. Rigby's _____ as the team leader at the archeological dig, she found the remains of a 3,000-year-old doll that had probably been _____ on by a child living in the clean, _____ forest circling the mountain. In addition, the team found evidence that the ancient tribe knew how to _____ weapons and tools by hammering layers of steel together to add strength, but the laboratory would have to test the tools in order to _____ the theory.

Exercise II

Sentence Completion

Complete the sentence in a way that shows you understand the meaning of the italicized vocabulary word.

1. The family lived a life of *penury* after…
    the parents lossed their jobs

2. The children exhibited total *exuberance* when…
    they got 1000 pieces of candy

3. The *gothic* architecture of the castle is characteristic of…
    Wednesday.

4. Don't let the size of the players *daunt* you; they're not…
    good at playing

5. Linda *girded* herself against the swarm of killer bees by…
    putting long sleeves & pants on.

6. When Connie saw the *cadaverous* refugees, she immediately…
    ran away.

7. The wealthy industrialist was born in a *hovel*, but he…
    finally got enough $ to get a mansion.

8. If Amy had not found an *egress* from the burning house, she…
    would've been stuck in house.

9. Because of the *flux* in the number of customers, Sal didn't know if his
    restaurant would…
    be sucessful.

10. The *despot* ordered his guards to…
    guard him.

11. The artifact differed from other *primeval* artifacts because…
    it looked modern?

12. Carol *doted* on the ugly little dog ever since…
    t gave him a kiss

13. The professor's *tenure* was cut short because…
    he was getting old,

14. Sean *laminated* his school ID card because…
    he didn't want it 2 get dirty

15. Only an eyewitness could *substantiate* the…
    what had happen.

Exercise III

Roots, Prefixes, and Suffixes

Study the entries and answer the questions that follow.

The suffix –*ism* means "belief in."
The root *deci* means "ten."
The prefix *anti*– means "against."
The roots *duc* and *duct* mean "to lead."
The root *do* means "to give."

1. Using *literal* translations as guidance, define the following words without using a dictionary:

    A. idealism   D. objectivism
    B. abduct   E. duct
    C. donate   F. pardon

2. A medicine that works against certain symptoms by taking them away is called a[n] _____. A battleship might have _____ guns for use against enemy planes.

3. A[n] _____ is a ten-year period, and the word that originally meant "to kill every tenth person" is _____.

4. List as many words as you can think of that contain the roots *duc* or *duct*.

Exercise IV

Inference

Complete the sentence by inferring information about the italicized word from its context.

1. In order to *daunt* the child's desire to play with matches...

2. A homeless person living in *penury* would probably appreciate...

3. If a city experiences a severe *flux* in population, then people are...

Exercise V

Writing

Here is a writing prompt similar to the one you will find on the writing portion of an assessment test.

Plan and write an essay based on the following statement:

> It was one of the significant declarations of an English critic and moralist who said that conduct is three fourths of life. A writer on psychology said that three fourths of our daily conduct consists in simply taking off the brakes and letting ideas and impulses have their way.
>
> –Anna Harris Smith, *Golden Words for Daily Counsel*, 1888

Assignment: Anna Harris Smith wrote this passage for a book that offers guidance on day-to-day life, but the two references seem to be contradictory. Do you agree with the first premise, the second premise, or a combination of the two? In an essay, explain which solution you favor as the ideal guidance for daily living. Support your position with evidence from your reading, classroom studies, experience, and observation.

Thesis: Write a *one-sentence* response to the assignment. Make certain this single sentence offers a clear statement of your position.

Example: The philosophy of the moralist, that conduct is three fourths of life, is correct because the average person must interact with other people most of the day, and any interaction is conduct.

_____

_____

Organizational Plan: List at least three subtopics you will use to support your main idea. This list is your outline.

1. _____

2. _____

3. _____

Draft: Following your outline, write a good first draft of your essay. Remember to support all your points with examples, facts, references to reading, etc.

Review and Revise: Exchange essays with a classmate. Using the scoring guide for Word Choice on page 255, score your partner's essay (while he or she scores yours). Focus on word choice and the use of language conventions. If necessary, rewrite your essay to improve word choice and/or your use of language.

Exercise VI

Improving Paragraphs

Read the following passage and then answer the multiple-choice questions that follow. The questions will require you to make decisions regarding the revision of the reading selection.

1   (1) Plaid may not be exactly what you think it is. (2) Tartan may be what you think plaid is.

2   (3) Autumn usually finds us wrapped in a tartan, whether they are around our torsos, our legs, or a combination of both. (4) The use of a "plaid" seems to come into fashion every autumn and can be a handsome addition to any outfit. (5) Warmth is a bonus of wearing a plaid, no matter what design it is.

3   (6) A plaid, you see, is a woven piece of fabric worn over the shoulder sometimes tucked under a belt to hold it in place. (7) The design of various colored stripes crossing at right angles is rightfully a tartan, many a plaid is a tartan design.

4   (8) The autumn is a great time of the year to purchase a favorite tartan and sew a lovely long skirt for informal entertaining at home. (9) The closet must be full of soft old shirts of particular tartans to wrap around our shoulders for a quick trip to the post office. (10) The design is an old favorite for ties and scarves, lap robes and carriage covers for baby's stroller. (11) Some believe that the tartan design originated as a way to incorporate expensive, dyed threads in cheap materials. (12) No matter what you choose to tailor, it is guaranteed to be an eye-catching, original design.

5   (13) If you have a yen for pretty colors and patterns with classic lines, feel free to make yourself a plaid with knotted tassels on the edge. (14) Wear it for warmth and style as you enjoy the autumn weather. (15) If you have a fear of tying knots, then buy a huge tartan scarf and throw it over your shoulder with a flair for flamboyance.

1. Which of the following suggestions would improve the development of the passage?
    A.   Exchange paragraphs 1 and 3.
    B.   Exchange paragraphs 2 and 3.
    C.   Exchange paragraphs 1 and 4.
    D.   Exchange paragraphs 1 and 2.
    E.   Exchange paragraphs 1 and 5.

2. Which of the following describes the error in paragraph 2?
    A.   run-on sentence
    B.   spelling error
    C.   sentence fragment
    D.   improper pronoun and antecedent agreement
    E.   incorrect prepositional phrase

3. Which of the following would correct the error in paragraph 3?
   A. Combine sentences 6 and 7.
   B. Capitalize *tartan*.
   C. Make two sentences out of sentence 6.
   D. Delete "you see."
   E. Add *and* after the comma in sentence 7.

4. Which of the following should be deleted from paragraph 4?
   A. sentence 8
   B. sentence 9
   C. sentence 10
   D. sentence 11
   E. sentence 12

5. Which of the following changes would best improve the order of the concluding paragraph?
   A. Start the paragraph with sentence 15.
   B. Exchange sentences 13 and 14.
   C. Exchange sentences 14 and 15.
   D. Include a sentence about autumn weather.
   E. Explain the difference between plaid and tartan.

Lesson Eight

1. **gaunt**   (gônt)   *adj.*   very thin and bony, especially from sickness
After 21 days without a real meal, the *gaunt* miners emerged from the collapsed mineshaft and squinted beneath the blinding sunlight.
syn: emaciated; haggard   *ant: plump*

2. **undue**   (un dōō′)   *adj.*   inappropriately excessive
Bob refused to give *undue* thanks to the officer who just wrote him a parking ticket.
syn: unnecessary; needless   *ant: necessary; appropriate*

3. **guerilla**   (gə ril′ ə)   *n.*   a member of an independent band of soldiers that engages in raids and surprise attacks
The government secured the capital city after the rebellion, but *guerillas* continued to raid villages and attack convoys for several years.
syn: irregular; insurgent

4. **mire**   (mī′ ər)   *n.*   muddy, swampy ground
The crew escaped the crashed jet just before it sank completely into the swampy *mire*.
syn: quagmire; bog

5. **sector**   (sek′ tər)   *n.*   a part or division
When workers in the private *sector* lose jobs, there is less money available to pay government workers.
syn: branch; category

6. **beget**   (bi get′, bē)   *v.*   to produce; to make happen
Hatred *begets* more hatred.
syn: generate   *ant: prevent*

7. **educe**   (i dōōs′)   *v.*   to draw or bring out
The lawyer tried to *educe* a response from the witness.
syn: elicit   *ant: suppress*

8. **glean**   (glēn)   *v.*   to collect bit by bit; to gather with patient labor
The investigator *gleaned* pertinent information from the witnesses to the crash.
syn: garner   *ant: disperse*

9. **chafe**   (chāf)   *v.*   to wear or irritate, often through rubbing or friction
The freezing wind *chafed* our faces as we struggled through the storm.

10. **effrontery** (i frun´ tə rē)   *n.*   shameless boldness
    The thief had the *effrontery* to demand a reward for returning the money
    he had stolen.
    syn: impudence; nerve; audacity   *ant: timidity*

11. **imbibe** (im bīb´)   *v.*   to drink; to absorb into the body
    After the raid, the Vikings feasted and *imbibed* to the point of physical sickness.

12. **feign** (fān)   *v.*   to pretend
    He *feigned* an interest in the conversation, but his mind wandered elsewhere.
    syn: simulate; fake

13. **desist** (di sist´, dē)   *v.*   to stop; to discontinue
    The police ordered the rioters to *desist* before someone got hurt.
    syn: cease; end   *ant: begin; start*

14. **allude** (ə lōōd´)   *v.*   to hint at; to refer to indirectly
    The attorney *alluded* to a cover-up without actually mentioning it.
    syn: suggest; imply   *ant: expose*

15. **elite** (ē lēt´, ā, i)   *n.*   the choice members or best of a group
    Soldiers in the Special Forces are part of the military's *elite*.
    syn: leaders   *ant: common; multitude*

Exercise I

Words in Context

From the list below, supply the words needed to complete the paragraph. Some words will not be used.

beget	imbibe	chafe	feign
desist	glean	effrontery	educe

1. The psychologist used a form of hypnotism to _____ her patient's childhood memories. Little by little, the doctor _____ clues that might _____ the solution to Kate's disorder. Originally, the doctor worried that Kate would _____ compliance and simply pretend to remember things, but the doctor could tell that the memories were real by the way in which they seemed to _____ the patient emotionally. One hour was all Kate could stand before her therapy had to _____ for the day.

From the list below, supply the words needed to complete the paragraph. Some words will not be used.

effrontery	beget	elite	imbibe
allude	guerilla		

2. As usual, the senator's cocktail party was a gathering of the society's _____. Some guests mingled and chatted about politics while they _____ fine wine, but others demonstrated a social _____ by first eating and then criticizing the host's menu selections. The critics never actually said they didn't enjoy the food, of course; they merely _____ to the host's questionable choice of caterer.

From the list below, supply the words needed to complete the paragraph. Some words will not be used.

gaunt	effrontery	mire	guerilla
sector	undue	chafe	

3. The _____ have been at war with the regime for two years, and the hardship of living in a remote _____ of the mountains has taken its toll. Starvation and constant movement have given the young soldiers _____ faces. To save supplies, the rebels avoid any _____ activity, and they travel only through the _____ of the lowlands, where the regime cannot pursue them with heavy military machines without sinking in the mud.

Exercise II

Sentence Completion

Complete the sentence in a way that shows you understand the meaning of the italicized vocabulary word.

1. The councilman was concerned that a pool hall would *beget*…

2. Members of the school's academic *elite* were chosen to…

3. From her moving story, the author hoped that readers would *educe*…

4. Without actually saying what was wrong with the program, Beth *alluded* to…

5. Jaime *gleaned* as much information about painting as she could before she…

6. The teacher told the students that if they didn't *desist*, they would…

7. The criminal complained that his handcuffs *chafed*…

8. Neil *feigned* sickness in an effort to…

9. In a display of *effrontery*, the waiter…

10. The festive bunch feasted and *imbibed* after…

11. Ryan became *gaunt* during…

12. To prevent *undue* panic in an emergency, teachers are supposed to…

13. The *guerillas* were almost impossible to defeat because…

14. The only way to escape from the *mire* is…

15. Connie's job in the environmental *sector* requires her to…

Exercise III

Roots, Prefixes, and Suffixes

Study the entries and answer the questions that follow.

The root *termin* means "end" or "boundary."
The root *ver* means "true."
The roots *dem* and *demos* mean "people."

1. Using *literal* translations as guidance, define the following words without using a dictionary:

   A. terminal   D. verify
   B. terminate   E. verdict
   C. exterminate   F. democracy

2. When many people contract a disease, it is said to be a[n] _____. If *gogue* means "to lead," then a *demagogue* is _____.

3. List as many words as you can think of that contain the root *term*.

Exercise IV

Inference

Complete the sentence by inferring information about the italicized word from its context.

1. If someone *feigns* sleep, then he or she…

2. Instead of *alluding* to her dislike of the video game, Karen…

3. If the school wants a particular activity to *desist*, it must want…

Exercise V

Critical Reading

Below is a pair of reading passages followed by several multiple-choice questions. Carefully read the passages and choose the best answer for each of the questions.

The first passage is an excerpt from Rebecca Harding Davis's "Life in the Iron Mills," a description of life and living conditions during the early stages of American industry. The second passage is an excerpt from Charles Dickens's Hard Times, *a Victorian novel set in the fictional industrial city of Coketown, England.*

Passage 1

A CLOUDY DAY: do you know what that is in a town of iron-works? The sky sank down before dawn, muddy, flat, immovable. The air is thick, clammy with the breath of crowded human beings. It stifles me. I open the window, and, looking out, can scarcely see through the rain the grocer's shop opposite, where a crowd of drunken Irishmen are puffing Lynchburg tobacco in their pipes. I can detect the scent through all the foul smells ranging loose in the air.

The idiosyncrasy of this town is smoke. It rolls sullenly in slow folds from the great chimneys of the iron-founderies, and settles down in black, slimy pools on the muddy streets. Smoke on the wharves, smoke on the dingy boats, on the yellow river,—clinging in a coating of greasy soot to the house-front, the two faded poplars, the faces of the passers-by. The long train of mules, dragging masses of pig-iron through the narrow street, have a foul vapor hanging to their reeking sides. Here, inside, is a little broken figure of an angel pointing upward from the mantel-shelf; but even its wings are covered with smoke, clotted and black. Smoke everywhere! A dirty canary chirps desolately in a cage beside me. Its dream of green fields and sunshine is a very old dream,—almost worn out, I think.

From the back-window I can see a narrow brick-yard sloping down to the river-side, strewed with rain-butts and tubs. The river, dull and tawny-colored, *(la belle riviere!)* drags itself sluggishly along, tired of the heavy weight of boats and coal-barges. What wonder? When I was a child, I used to fancy a look of weary, dumb appeal upon the face of the negro-like river slavishly bearing its burden day after day. Something of the same idle notion comes to me today, when from the street-window I look on the slow stream of human life creeping past, night and morning, to the great mills. Masses of men, with dull, besotted faces bent to the ground, sharpened here and there by pain or cunning; skin and muscle and flesh begrimed with smoke and ashes; stooping all night over boiling caldrons of metal, laired by day in dens of drunkenness and infamy; breathing from infancy to death an air saturated with fog and grease and soot, vileness for soul and body. What do you make of a case like that, amateur psychologist? You call it an altogether serious thing to be alive: to these men it is a drunken jest, a joke,—horrible to angels perhaps, to them commonplace enough. My fancy about the river was an idle one: it is no type of such a life. What if it be stagnant and slimy here? It knows that beyond there waits for it odorous sunlight,—quaint old gardens, dusky with soft, green foliage of apple-trees, and flushing crimson with roses,—air, and fields, and mountains. The future of the Welsh puddler passing just now is not so pleasant. To be stowed away, after his grimy work is done, in a hole in the muddy graveyard, and after that,—*not* air, nor green fields, nor curious roses.

Passage 2

It was a town of red brick, or of brick that would have been red if the smoke and ashes had allowed it; but as matters stood it was a town of unnatural red and black like the painted face of a savage. It was a town of machinery and tall chimneys, out of which interminable serpents of smoke trailed themselves for ever and ever, and never got uncoiled. It had a black
5   canal in it, and a river that ran purple with ill-smelling dye, and vast piles of building full of windows where there was a rattling and a trembling all day long, and where the piston of the steam-engine worked monotonously up and down like the head of an elephant in a state of melancholy madness. It contained several large streets all very like one another, and many small streets still more like one another, inhabited by people equally like one another, who all
10 went in and out at the same hours, with the same sound upon the same pavements, to do the same work, and to whom every day was the same as yesterday and tomorrow, and every year the counterpart of the last and the next.

These attributes of Coketown were in the main inseparable from the work by which it was sustained; against them were to be set off, comforts of life which found their way all over
15 the world, and elegancies of life which made, we will not ask how much of the fine lady, who could scarcely bear to hear the place mentioned. The rest of its features were voluntary, and they were these.

You saw nothing in Coketown but what was severely workful. If the members of a religious persuasion built a chapel there—as the members of eighteen religious persuasions
20 had done—they made it a pious warehouse of red brick, with sometimes (but this is only in highly ornamental examples) a bell in a birdcage on the top of it. The solitary exception was the New Church; a stuccoed edifice with a square steeple over the door, terminating in four short pinnacles like florid wooden legs. All the public inscriptions in the town were painted alike, in severe characters of black and white. The jail might have been the infirmary, the infirmary
25 might have been the jail, the town-hall might have been either, or both, or anything else, for anything that appeared to the contrary in the graces of their construction. [. . .]

No. Coketown did not come out of its own furnaces, in all respects like gold that had stood the fire. First, the perplexing mystery of the place was, Who belonged to the eighteen denominations? Because, whoever did, the labouring people did not. It was very strange to
30 walk through the streets on a Sunday morning, and note how few of them the barbarous jangling of bells that was driving the sick and nervous mad, called away from their own quarter, from their own close rooms, from the corners of their own streets, where they lounged listlessly, gazing at all the church and chapel going, as at a thing with which they had no manner of concern. Nor was it merely the stranger who noticed this, because there was a native organi-
35 zation in Coketown itself, whose members were to be heard of in the House of Commons every session, indignantly petitioning for acts of parliament that should make these people religious by main force. Then came the Teetotal Society, who complained that these same people would get drunk, and showed in tabular statements that they did get drunk, and proved at tea parties that no inducement, human or Divine (except a medal), would induce them to forego their
40 custom of getting drunk. Then came the chemist and druggist, with other tabular statements, showing that when they didn't get drunk, they took opium. Then came the experienced chaplain of the jail, with more tabular statements, outdoing all the previous tabular statements, and showing that the same people would resort to low haunts, hidden from the public eye, where they heard low singing and saw low dancing, and mayhap joined in it; and where A. B., aged
45 twenty-four next birthday, and committed for eighteen months' solitary, had himself said (not that he had ever shown himself particularly worthy of belief) his ruin began, as he was perfectly sure and confident that otherwise he would have been a tip-top moral specimen.

1A. The overall tone of the first passage can best be described as
    A. joyous.
    B. nostalgic.
    C. disheartening.
    D. ironic.
    E. condemning.

1B. Which details from passage 1 best support your answer to question 1A?
    A. mules, stream of human life, odorous sunlight
    B. smoke, masses of men, great mills
    C. quaint old gardens, soft foliage, apple trees
    D. slimy pools, foul vapor, muddy graveyard
    E. besotted faces, Welsh puddler, pig-iron

2A. As used in line 6 of the first passage, *idiosyncrasy* most nearly means
    A. downfall.
    B. savior.
    C. dogma.
    D. distinction.
    E. transformation.

2B. Which choice best describes the method Davis uses to emphasize the answer to question 2A?
    A. the two fragments
    B. logical reasoning
    C. changing tone
    D. repetition
    E. relating to the audience

3A. What is the author's intention in personifying smoke in the beginning of the second paragraph of passage 1?
    A. to describe the pollution of the town
    B. to emphasize the annoying effects of the smoke
    C. to introduce the smoke as a character telling the story
    D. to make the smoke appear benevolent
    E. to describe the town from the smoke's point of view

3B. Which phrase from paragraph 2 best supports your answer to question 3A?
    A. rolls sullenly
    B. on the wharves
    C. reeking sides
    D. covered with smoke
    E. foul vapor hanging

4A. As a child, the author of the first passage imagined the river to have a "weary, dumb appeal." What does she look upon in the same way as an adult?
   A.   the mill town
   B.   the people's walking to and from work
   C.   the smoke's rolling into the town
   D.   the grocer's shop
   E.   the canary

4B. In passage 1, why is the author's youthful perception of the river ultimately incorrect?
   A.   The river cannot recover from its condition, while people can.
   B.   The river is not as polluted as she thought it was.
   C.   The river is not a river, but a manmade canal that carries waste from the mill.
   D.   The river sustains the most damage from the mill, rendering it unable to carry burdens.
   E.   The river has hope because it merely passes through the miserable town.

5A. As it is used in passage 1, lines 19 and 28, *idle* most nearly means
   A.   stopped.
   B.   young.
   C.   bored.
   D.   flowing.
   E.   meaningless.

5B. The best support for the answer to question 5A is
   A.   *idle*'s relation to the word *fancy.*
   B.   the author's use of *idle* to discredit her notion.
   C.   the fact that the author uses *idle* twice.
   D.   the author's use of *idle* as a child.
   E.   the author's use of *idle* to describe a stagnant river.

6A. Dickens, the author of the second passage, probably uses the simile in lines 2-3 to
   A.   convey his dislike of savages.
   B.   imply that savages are employed as plant workers.
   C.   describe the way in which the smoke drifts.
   D.   contradict the industrial setting with primitive imagery.
   E.   suggest that Coketown is a colony of England.

6B. Which types of details from passage 2 best support your answer to question 6A?
   A.   serpents of smoke, elephant
   B.   unnatural red, vast piles
   C.   madness, large streets
   D.   machinery, tall chimneys
   E.   black canal, piston

7A. Which of the following best paraphrases lines 8-12 of the second passage?
  A. The monotonous town had no unique people or characteristics.
  B. Coketown had good days and bad days.
  C. Time passed slowly in the town.
  D. All people enjoyed equal treatment in the town.
  E. Coketown was very orderly.

7B. Which line from passage 1 most resembles lines 8-12 from passage 2?
  A. "The idiosyncrasy of this town is smoke."
  B. "...long train of mules, dragging masses of pig-iron through the narrow street..."
  C. "...I look on the slow stream of human life creeping past, night and morning... Masses of men, with dull, besotted faces bent to the ground..."
  D. "The river, dull and tawny-colored...drags itself sluggishly along, tired of the heavy weight of boats and coal-barges."
  E. "...to these men it is a drunken jest, a joke,—horrible to angels perhaps, to them commonplace enough."

8A. According to both passages, which is a characteristic of the residents of industrial towns?
  A. People use the rivers to get to work.
  B. The people have no hope of leaving the town.
  C. The people live routine lives in unhealthy environments.
  D. Most of the factory workers enjoy their jobs.
  E. Most of the people have soot on their faces.

8B. Both passages address religion to some degree and its relevance to the laborers. Passage 1 contrasts the laborers with "angels." The "angels" in line 27, passage 1, are most similar to which people from passage 2?
  A. the machines
  B. the bar owners
  C. members of Coketown's "native organizations"
  D. the laboring people
  E. the general public

9A. As it is used in passage 2, line 16, the word *voluntary* most nearly means
  A. accidental.
  B. organized.
  C. coincidental.
  D. extreme.
  E. intentional.

9B. Using the same definition for *voluntary* that you used to answer question 9A, which detail of passage 1 can be described as *voluntary*?
  A. smoke
  B. greasy soot
  C. slimy pools
  D. great mills
  E. yellow river

10A. Which of the following best describes a difference in theme between the two passages?
   A.   Passage 1 is about nature, and passage 2 is about social class.
   B.   Passage 1 is about industry, and passage 2 is about colonization.
   C.   Passage 1 is about pollution, and passage 2 is about slavery.
   D.   Passage 1 is about acceptance, and passage 2 is about industry.
   E.   Passage 1 is about social class, and passage 2 is about wealth.

10B. Which choice best describes the difference in the people portrayed in both passages?
   A.   Passage 2 likens the laborers to slaves.
   B.   Passage 1 portrays only laborers, while passage 2 includes other classes of people.
   C.   Passage 2 suggests that laborers are religious.
   D.   Passage 1 portrays laborers as able to escape their misery.
   E.   Passage 2 suggests positive effects of industry on the people of the town.

Lesson Nine

1. **bilk** (bilk) *v.* to cheat or swindle; to thwart
   The landscapers tried to *bilk* the homeowner out of money by charging for work that was never authorized.
   syn: defraud; con

2. **homily** (hom´ ə lē) *n.* a sermon
   "Sir," I said, "if I may interrupt you, I need food and clothing for these people, not a *homily* on patience."
   syn: lecture; speech

3. **demise** (di mīz´) *n.* death; a ceasing to exist
   Mary will inherit the estate upon the *demise* of Uncle Irving.
   syn: termination; conclusion

4. **emit** (ē mit´) *v.* to send out; to give forth, as in sound or light
   The lamp did not *emit* enough light for reading.
   syn: produce; discharge; release

5. **decadence** (dek´ ə dəns) *n.* moral deterioration
   It is often suggested that Rome fell as a result of its own *decadence*.
   syn: decay; corruption; debauchery   *ant: decency*

6. **aghast** (ə gast´) *adj.* feeling great dismay or horror
   We were *aghast* when we saw how disrespectfully the teenager treated her parents.
   syn: terrified; horrified; shocked

7. **granary** (gran´ nə rē, grā) *n.* a storehouse for grain
   We lost a year's supply of corn when the *granary* burned down.

8. **choleric** (kə lə´ rik, kä´) *adj.* easily angered
   He was a *choleric* man, whose temper often got him into trouble.
   syn: irascible; cantankerous   *ant: apathetic; impassive*

9. **impede** (im pēd´) *v.* to hinder; to obstruct
   The reckless fan's running through the outfield *impeded* the conclusion of the playoff game.
   syn: delay; retard   *ant: aid; encourage*

10. **qualm** (kwäm) *n.* a feeling of uneasiness
    The boy had no *qualms* about cheating on the test.
    syn: misgiving   *ant: ease*

11. **lampoon** (lam pōōn′) *n.* a written satire used to ridicule or attack someone
The *lampoon* of the athletic program in the school newspaper angered the players and the coach.
syn: parody; caricature

12. **narcissistic** (när si sis′ tik) *adj.* conceited; having excessive self-love or admiration
The *narcissistic* criminal cared only about his own fate.
syn: vain; egotistic   *ant: humble; modest*

13. **eradicate** (i rad′ i kāt) *v.* to wipe out; to destroy
The pest control specialist *eradicated* the termites in our house.
syn: eliminate   *ant: add; create*

14. **fabricate** (fab′ ri kāt) *v.* to concoct; to make up a story in order to deceive
The scientist's career ended when someone discovered that he had *fabricated* his experiments.
syn: forge; fake

15. **ghastly** (gast′ lē) *adj.* horrible; frightful
The *ghastly* smile on the dead man at the end of the movie showed that he had enjoyed the last laugh.
syn: dreadful; hideous   *ant: lovely; attractive*

Exercise I

Words in Context

From the list below, supply the words needed to complete the paragraph. Some words will not be used.

decadence	homily	bilk	narcissistic
choleric	qualm	fabricate	

1. The reverend had _____ what he thought was an excellent story for his weekly _____. It was a lengthy parable about a wealthy family that lived in _____ and had no _____ about their lavish lifestyle or mistreatment of servants. The sermon went fairly well until the _____ preacher angrily stopped in mid-sentence to lecture a sleeping member of the congregation.

From the list below, supply the words needed to complete the paragraph. Some words will not be used.

impede	lampoon	demise	granary
ghastly	emit	qualm	

2. Bill arrived at the _____ with his truckload of wheat and with a[n] _____ look on his face. Apparently, the old railroad crossing lights had failed to _____ a signal, and Bill had stopped just in time to postpone his _____. The next time he has to drive over railroad tracks, Bill declared, he is going to stop his truck and look both ways, even if he _____ the flow of traffic.

From the list below, supply the words needed to complete the paragraph. Some words will not be used.

narcissistic	bilk	decadence	eradicate
lampoon	aghast	choleric	

3. The author claimed that her article was fiction, but it was actually a[n] _____ that satirized the life of a famous Hollywood figure. It portrayed the famous director as being so _____ that he had mirrors in every room of his mansion so that he could observe his own "perfection" at any moment. It also portrayed the movie mogul as someone who _____ investors out of their money by knowingly creating box-office failures while pocketing millions. The director was _____ when he read the derisive-but-truthful satire of himself. Within minutes, he was on the phone with his lawyers trying to stop the magazine before the article _____ whatever remained of his credibility.

Exercise II

Sentence Completion

Complete the sentence in a way that shows you understand the meaning of the italicized vocabulary word.

1. The gauge on the dashboard *emits* a red light when…

2. If the *granary* fills up too early, the farmers will have to…

3. The late night show included *lampoons* that were meant to…

4. Larry had no *qualms* about…

5. During the *homily*, Jonathan Edwards warned the congregation that…

6. The *demise* of the old West can be attributed to…

7. The *choleric* sailor often found himself in the brig for…

8. *Narcissistic* people seldom worry about…

9. You could tell by the *ghastly* look on her face that she…

10. Some of the games at the carnival are designed to *bilk* people by…

11. You will *impede* the healing of your broken foot if you…

12. *Decadence* among government officials ultimately caused…

13. You will be *aghast* when you see…

14. Dan tried to *eradicate*…

15. Heidi *fabricated* an excuse for…

Exercise III

Roots, Prefixes, and Suffixes

Study the entries and answer the questions that follow.

The root *multi* means "many."
The roots *naut* and *naus* mean "sailor" or "ship."
The roots *nov* and *neo* mean "new."

1. Using *literal* translations as guidance, define the following words without using a dictionary:

A.	innovation	D.	multitude
B.	novel	E.	multimedia
C.	nautical	F.	neoclassical

2. Someone who is new at a sport is said to be a[n] _____. If you restore an old house to new condition, then you _____ it.

3. Someone who is not used to sailing might get _____, or seasick, on his or her first voyage. A sailor explores or travels the seas, but a[n] _____ travels through space.

4. List as many words as you can think of that contain the roots *multi* or *nov*.

Exercise IV

Inference

Complete the sentence by inferring information about the italicized word from its context.

1. A *narcissistic* person might refuse to help someone because...

2. If you have *qualms* about doing something, then you might...

3. People who cannot control their wants and pursue lives of *decadence* are in danger of...

Exercise V

Writing

Here is a writing prompt similar to the one you will find on the writing portion of an assessment test.

Plan and write an essay based on the following statement:

> Now if I am to be no mere copper wire amateur but a luminous author, I must also be a most intensely refractory person, liable to go out and to go wrong at inconvenient moments, and with incendiary possibilities. These are the faults of my qualities; and I assure you that I sometimes dislike myself so much that when some irritable reviewer chances at that moment to pitch into me with zest, I feel unspeakably relieved and obliged.
>
> –G. Bernard Shaw
> from an "immoderately long letter"
> to Arthur Bingham Walkley in 1903

Assignment: The above passage is from a letter that George Bernard Shaw submitted with his manuscript for *Man and Superman*. In an essay, explain why Shaw would feel "relieved and obliged" if his work were to endure harsh criticism. Support your explanation with evidence from your knowledge, classroom studies, experience and observation.

Thesis: Write a *one-sentence* response to the assignment. Make certain this single sentence offers a clear statement of your position.

Example: George Bernard Shaw knows that his own work is sometimes offensive or controversial, and it relieves him to hear that other people perceive it in that way—just as he planned.

_____

_____

Organizational Plan: List at least three subtopics you will use to support your main idea. This list is your outline.

1. _____

2. _____

3. _____

Draft: Following your outline, write a good first draft of your essay. Remember to support all your points with examples, facts, references to reading, etc.

Review and Revise: Exchange essays with a classmate. Using the Holistic scoring guide on page 256, score your partner's essay (while he or she scores yours). If necessary, rewrite your essay to correct the problems noted by your partner.

Exercise VI

English Practice

Identifying Sentence Errors

Identify the grammatical error in each of the following sentences. If the sentence contains no error, select answer choice E.

1. My oldest <u>sister, Marilyn</u> a talented <u>commercial artist,</u> <u>is also</u> a
           (A)   (B)   (C)
    <u>registered nurse.</u>   <u>No error</u>
       (D)   (E)

2. <u>Arguing with</u> a professor <u>in class</u> <u>will wreck havoc</u>
       (A)   (B)   (C)
    <u>with your grade.</u>   <u>No error</u>
       (D)   (E)

3. If the <u>repaired car</u> <u>were ready</u> to <u>be driven,</u> we <u>would of taken</u>
         (A)   (B)   (C)   (D)
    it home.   <u>No error</u>
           (E)

4. <u>The nurse</u> <u>suddenly jumps</u> <u>when the doctor</u> walked through the door
      (A)   (B)   (C)
    <u>to the operating room.</u>   <u>No error</u>
        (D)   (E)

5. I <u>do not like</u> <u>Shelly playing</u> the stereo <u>so loudly</u> <u>in the car.</u>   <u>No error</u>
       (A)   (B)   (C)   (D)   (E)

Improving Sentences

The underlined portion of each sentence below contains some flaw. Select the answer choice that best corrects the flaw.

6. <u>I could watch the lake all day long playing computer solitaire is my only distraction.</u>
    A. While I could watch the lake all day long and playing computer solitaire is my only distraction.
    B. All day long playing computer solitaire is my only distraction when I could be watching the lake.
    C. Playing computer solitaire all day long, watching the lake is my only distraction.
    D. My only distraction playing computer solitaire all day long is watching the lake.
    E. I could watch the lake all day long. Playing computer solitaire is my only distraction.

7. Lisa was a girl who had to be in trouble before she would <u>turn the other cheek.</u>
    A. get into a boat.
    B. learn to float on her back.
    C. back down.
    D. make a stitch in time.
    E. take a turn for the worse.

8. <u>The dog was released by Stephanie and the guests were startled by the cheese platter when that was knocked on the floor by it.</u>
    A. Stephanie released the dog and it startled the guests when the cheese platter was knocked onto the floor.
    B. When Stephanie released the dog, it knocked the guests onto the floor with the cheese platter.
    C. The dog startled the guests when, released, it knocked the cheese platter onto the floor.
    D. Stephanie released the dog, and it startled the guests when it knocked the cheese platter onto the floor.
    E. Stephanie released the dog and the guests were startled when it knocked the cheese platter onto the floor.

9. <u>Some teenagers were suspended for failing grades this year on Monday.</u>
    A. This year some teenagers were suspended for failing grades on Monday.
    B. On Monday, some teenagers were suspended for having failing grades this year.
    C. For failing grades Monday, some teenagers were suspended this year.
    D. For having grades that failed this year, some teenagers were suspended on Monday.
    E. Suspended for failing grades this year on Monday were some teenagers.

10. Henry bought a new computer that has a large memory <u>and having a DVD burner.</u>
    A. and a DVD burner.
    B. that has a DVD burner.
    C. for the DVD burner.
    D. and it has a DVD burner.
    E. with a DVD burner.

Review Lessons 7-9

Exercise I

Inferences

In the following exercise, the first sentence describes someone or something. Infer information from the first sentence, and then choose the word from the Word Bank that best completes the second sentence.

bilk	glean	emit	substantiate
decadence	feign	tenure	exuberance

1. The explorers eagerly ate the gruel offered by the poor, undernourished nomads, even though they were not hungry and the mush had a repulsive taste.

   From this sentence, we can infer that the explorers _____ gratitude out of respect for the nomads' hospitality.

2. The heirs to the oil baron's fortune bought mansions, cars, and other luxuries with reckless abandon until the fortune had dwindled to nothing.

   From this sentence, we can infer that the heirs squandered the fortune by living lives of _____.

3. Video recordings proved that the suspect was not, in fact, at the scene of the crime, just like he had claimed.

   From this sentence, we can infer that the videos _____ the suspect's alibi.

4. Kenneth invested his life savings with Bernie, but never saw a penny of it again, even after Bernie ended up in prison.

   From this sentence, we can infer that Bernie _____ Kenneth out of his money.

5. Chad caused a traffic accident on his first day as a bus driver, and his company promptly fired him.

   From this sentence, we can infer that Chad had a short _____ as a bus driver.

Exercise II

Related Words

Some of the vocabulary words from Lessons 7 through 9 have related meanings. Complete the following sentences by choosing the word that best fits the context, based on information you infer from the use of the italicized word. Some word pairs will be antonyms, some will be synonyms, and some will simply be words often used in the same context.

1. The rookie's mocking remarks _____ the old police veteran so much in just ten minutes that the *choleric* patrolman exploded in a tirade about respect.
    A. alluded
    B. chafed
    C. bilked
    D. impeded
    E. doted

2. Any *undue* movement will _____ the hunt because the deer will flee if they notice even the slightest unnatural movement.
    A. desist
    B. emit
    C. lampoon
    D. impede
    E. feign

3. Wildlife officials on the island failed to _____ the invasive species of toad because each toad *begat* thousands of offspring.
    A. gird
    B. educe
    C. eradicate
    D. gratify
    E. substantiate

4. In her later years, the once-beloved queen became a _____ who ruled with cruelty and was dedicated only to building monuments that appeased her *narcissistic* self love.
    A. feign
    B. guerilla
    C. mandarin
    D. granary
    E. despot

5. Rations had become almost nonexistent during the siege, which left the villagers with _____ faces, and caused those suffering from typhoid to appear absolutely *cadaverous.*
    A. narcissistic
    B. primeval
    C. gaunt
    D. felonious
    E. gothic

6. The game design _____ of the software industry was so stressful that Caleb sought an *egress* to begin a new line of work.
   A. gist
   B. homily
   C. hovel
   D. mire
   E. sector

7. Caught off guard by the reporter's question, the mayoral candidate _____ knowledge of the subject and *fabricated* a story detailing his experience in dealing with the matter in question.
   A. feigned
   B. imbibed
   C. impeded
   D. daunted
   E. gleaned

8. No one understood why the multimillionaire built his six-story mansion amid the _____ of the slums, where his *decadence* seemed like a monumental insult.
   A. tenure
   B. penury
   C. insurrection
   D. egress
   E. effrontery

9. Try as she did to _____ her memory of the accident, the witness simply could not *substantiate* the driver's claim that a moose had caused the pileup.
   A. emit
   B. daunt
   C. educe
   D. impede
   E. allude

10. As the nights grew longer, the villagers *girded* themselves for winter by ensuring that the _____ contained enough wheat to feed both people and livestock until spring.
    A. granary
    B. qualm
    C. hovel
    D. fruition
    E. penury

> ## Exercise III

Deeper Meanings

Choose a word to replace the italicized word in each sentence. All of the possible choices for each sentence have similar definitions, but the correct answer will have a connotation that best suits the context. For example, the words "delete," "destroy," and "obliterate" all mean "to remove or wipe out," but no one would ever say, "I destroyed the name from the document." The correct choice will be the word that has the best specific meaning and does not render the sentence awkward in tone or content. When choices seem close, look for a clue in the context that makes one choice better than the other.

Note that the correct answer is not always the primary vocabulary word from the lesson.

aghast	poorness	leader	gaunt
hovel	startled	amused	situations
shelter	old	penury	despot
shrunken			

1. Many people lived in abject *need* after the economic depression collided with a nationwide drought, and jobs were all but nonexistent.

   Better word: _____

2. Marie was *disappointed* when she walked into the kitchen to find the family dog eating the 20-pound Thanksgiving turkey that she had spent all morning preparing for her many friends and relatives.

   Better word: _____

3. After years of neglect and considerable storm damage, the quaint *cottage* had become a sanctuary for raccoons, squirrels, and the occasional hiker looking to get out of the rain.

   Better word: _____

4. The cowboy's *narrow* face betrayed his arduous month on the range, where long days of labor in the sun and small meals had caused him to lose thirty pounds.

   Better word: _____

5. Ivan the Terrible became a harsh *ruler* later in his reign as czar, massacring people he deemed enemies, including members of his own family.

   Better word: _____

Exercise IV

Crossword Puzzle

Use the clues to complete the crossword puzzle. The answers consist of vocabulary words from Lessons 7 through 9.

Across

1. pretend
5. shelter for cereal
6. the way out
10. get in the way of
11. like a corpse
12. what a flashlight does to light
14. shocked and horrified
15. make afraid
16. dead end
18. pre-caveman

Down

2. tip the bottle
3. cares about me, me, me
4. what an exterminator does to roaches
7. soldier in a zoo?
8. shack by a track
9. make up
13. castle Dracula's decor
17. top notch

Exercise V

Subject Prompts

Here is a writing prompt similar to the one you will find on the writing portion of an assessment test. Follow the instructions below and write a brief, efficient essay.

The United States presently enjoys an all volunteer military, meaning that no one is forced into service or combat; however, several western nations presently enforce mandatory military or government service for all citizens (conscription).

Proponents of conscription claim that mandatory service for everyone will galvanize public awareness of news and politics because every person will have direct stake in what the military or government must do—especially in the context of engaging in war. Opponents refute the idea that conscription actually changes anything about the way in which nations go to war, citing unpopular wars in history that occurred when military service was indeed mandatory.

Should every citizen of a free nation be forced to participate in the government and or military, beyond simply voting for representatives, in order to enjoy the rights specified in the constitution? Argue your position and support your argument with at least three subtopics based on your observations, reading, or experiences.

Thesis: Write a *one-sentence* response to the above assignment. Make certain this single sentence offers a clear statement of your position.

Example: State service, either military or civilian, should be mandatory for anyone who wishes to receive the benefits of the nation.

_____

_____

Organizational Plan: List at least three subtopics you will use to support your main idea. This list is your outline.

1. _____

2. _____

3. _____

Draft: Following your outline, write a good first draft of your essay. Remember to support all your points with examples, facts, references to reading, etc.

Review and Revise: Exchange essays with a classmate. Using the scoring guide for Sentence Formation and Variety on page 254, score your partner's essay (while he or she scores yours). Focus on sentence structure and the use of language conventions. If necessary, rewrite your essay to improve the sentence structure and/or your use of language.

Lesson Ten

1. **fallible** (fal´ ə bəl) *adj.* capable of error
   All humans are *fallible* and sometimes make mistakes.
   syn: imperfect   *ant: infallible; flawless*

2. **blatant** (blā´ tent) *adj.* obvious; too conspicuous
   His *blatant* efforts to get the girl's attention were embarrassing to everyone.
   syn: unconcealed; deliberate   *ant: secretive; cautious*

3. **dawdle** (dô´ dəl) *v.* to waste time
   Bill, not wanting to go back to work, *dawdled* in the break room.
   syn: tarry; loiter   *ant: hasten; expedite*

4. **affiliate** (ə fil´ ē it) *n.* an associate; a partner
   He denied that he was an *affiliate* of any organized-crime families.
   syn: member; colleague

5. **fawn** (fôn) *v.* to act slavishly submissive
   Heartstruck fans *fawned* over the singer when he stepped off the stage during the concert.
   syn: grovel   *ant: ignore; disregard; neglect*

6. **calumny** (kal´ əm nē) *n.* a false and malicious accusation
   The candidate said that the accusation against him was a *calumny* meant to damage his reputation.
   syn: slander; slur   *ant: compliment*

7. **berate** (bi rāt´) *v.* to scold or rebuke severely and at length
   The coach *berated* the three players for arriving at the game late.
   syn: admonish; reprimand   *ant: praise*

8. **minion** (min´ yən) *n.* a submissive, servile follower
   The bully's *minions* obeyed him not out of loyalty, but out of fear.
   syn: lackey   *ant: leader*

9. **desolate** (des´ ə lit) *adj.* lonely; forlorn; uninhabited; barren
   The castaway spent four years on a *desolate* island, many miles from the mainland.
   syn: deserted; bleak   *ant: populous; cheerful*

10. **bane** (bān) *n.* the cause of ruin, harm, distress, or death
    The *bane* of the defeated alien invaders turned out to be the common cold.
    syn: blight; curse   *ant: aid; assistance*

11. **pacify** (pa´ sə fī)   *v.*   to calm down
    Grandmother was able to *pacify* the irritable baby.
    syn: appease; placate   *ant: provoke; agitate*

12. **garble** (gär´ bəl)   *v.*   to mix up or distort
    Jill's speech would have been good if she had not *garbled* the facts.
    syn: jumble; corrupt

13. **prevaricate** (pri vâr´ i kāt)   *v.*   to lie
    When asked about the crime, Jim *prevaricated* because he did not want to incriminate his friend.
    syn: hedge

14. **filch** (filch)   *v.*   to steal
    The woman *filched* my purse when I left the room to answer the telephone.
    syn: pilfer; rob

15. **neophyte** (nē´ ə fīt)   *n.*   a beginner
    Though Sara was a *neophyte* at golf, she outplayed most of the veterans.
    syn: novice; amateur   *ant: expert; veteran*

Exercise I

Words in Context

From the list below, supply the words needed to complete the paragraph. Some words will not be used.

calumny	dawdle	minion	prevaricate
bane	affiliate	garble	

1. To avoid prosecution, the crime boss relied on his _____ to do his dirty work for him. The _____ of the organization knew that if they were arrested, they took the fall alone; however, the boss's overconfidence in his associates proved to be his _____ when Knox, a hit man, testified against him in court. The boss claimed, of course, that the testimony was merely a spiteful _____ designed to embarrass him; however, the boss could not _____ cleverly enough to convince the jury that he was innocent.

From the list below, supply the words needed to complete the paragraph. Some words will not be used.

dawdle	minion	berate	blatant
filch	fawn	pacify	

2. Gina couldn't stand her friend's _____ attempt to get Lonnie to ask her to the dance. For weeks, Jamie _____ over Lonnie, even though he barely recognized her when they passed in the hall. Occasionally, Gina _____ her friend for being so foolish.

    "Don't _____ so much by waiting for him," Gina would say. "The dance is tomorrow; ask someone you actually know." Jamie usually got angry when Gina lectured her.

    "Will you leave me alone, please?" Gina often replied. "I'm almost ready to take my dog to the dance just to _____ you and your nagging."

From the list below, supply the words needed to complete the paragraph. Some words will not be used.

neophyte	bane	fallible	filch
garble	desolate	prevaricate	

3. "Even the most experienced hikers are _____ in climates as harsh as this one," said the desert guide as he turned and squinted at the miles of _____ sand dunes that stretched to the horizon. "If there's one message that I can't _____, it's to bring plenty of water. You _____ who haven't hiked in the desert before will soon learn that once you're out there in the dunes, water is nonexistent. What you manage to _____ from the various plants or from beneath the ground will not be enough to sustain you."

Exercise II

Sentence Completion

Complete the sentence in a way that shows you understand the meaning of the italicized vocabulary word.

1. *Affiliates* of the organization were invited to…

2. Craig *garbles* his speech when…

3. I'm just a *neophyte* at this card game, so please…

4. In a small town, spreading *calumny* about someone could…

5. That sports car is bound to be your *bane* if you continue to…

6. The *desolate* barn was the perfect place for…

7. If you *dawdle* all night, you won't…

8. The cab driver *berated* the pedestrian who…

9. Nicole learned that even computers can be *fallible* when she…

10. Some of the fans at the concert *fawned* over…

11. The pickpocket must have *filched* my wallet when he…

12. When asked by his wife how the new dress fit, Randy *prevaricated* because he thought…

13. Neil was asked to leave the restaurant after his *blatant* attempt to…

14. The crooked government official was never arrested because it was his *minions* who…

15. Jennie had to *pacify* her dog after it…

Exercise III

Roots, Prefixes, and Suffixes

Study the entries and answer the questions that follow.

The roots *corp* and *corpor* mean "body."
The root *rupt* means "to break."
The prefix *inter–* means "between" or "among."

1. Using *literal* translations as guidance, define the following words without using a dictionary:

A.	corporal	D.	interrupt
B.	corporation	E.	erupt
C.	incorporate	F.	corrupt

2. If someone's appendix *ruptures*, then it _____. If a bank has no money, then it can be described as _____.

3. List as many words as you can think of that contain the roots *corp*, or *rupt*, or the prefix *inter–*.

Exercise IV

Inference

Complete the sentence by inferring information about the italicized word from its context.

1. If you *dawdle* too long before leaving for the airport, you might…

2. Since Ben's answering machine *garbled* the incoming message, Ben did not…

3. If police are trying to *pacify* the crowd, then people in the crowd must be…

Exercise V

Critical Reading

Below is a reading passage followed by several multiple-choice questions. Carefully read the passage and choose the best answer for each of the questions.

"Federalist Number 1" is the first of a series of essays written between 1787 and 1788, which are now usually referred to as "The Federalist Papers." Intended to engage the American public in thought and encourage the states to ratify the new Constitution, those papers expound on the Constitution, emphasizing it as a way to prevent tyranny by majority factions through checks and balances in government. From the American Revolution to the ratification of the Constitution, not all Americans agreed that the Constitution was the proper solution to preventing tyranny. Alexander Hamilton addresses the problem in the following adaptation from "Federalist No. 1."

      Among the most formidable of the obstacles which the new Constitution will have to encounter may readily be distinguished the obvious interest of a certain class of men in every State to resist all changes which may hazard a diminution of the power, emolument, and consequence of the offices they hold under the State establishments; and the perverted ambition of

5   another class of men, who will either hope to aggrandize themselves by the confusions of their country, or will flatter themselves by **filching** fairer prospects of elevation from the subdivision of the empire into several partial confederacies than from its union under one government.

      It is not, however, my design to dwell upon observations of this nature. I am well aware that it would be disingenuous to resolve indiscriminately the opposition of any set of men (merely

10   because their situations might subject them to suspicion) into interested or ambitious views. Candor will oblige us to admit that even such men may be actuated by upright intentions; and it cannot be doubted that much of the opposition which has made its appearance, or may hereafter make its appearance, will spring from sources, blameless at least, if not respectable—the honest errors of minds led astray by preconceived jealousies and fears. So numerous indeed

15   and so powerful are the causes which serve to give a false bias to the judgment, that we, upon many occasions, see wise and good men on the wrong as well as on the right side of questions of the first magnitude to society. This circumstance, if duly attended to, would furnish a lesson of moderation to those who are ever so much persuaded of their being in the right in any controversy. And a further reason for caution, in this respect, might be drawn from the

20   reflection that we are not always sure that those who advocate the truth are influenced by purer principles than their antagonists. Ambition, avarice, personal animosity, party opposition, and many other motives not more laudable than these, are apt to operate as well upon those who support as those who oppose the right side of a question. Were there not even these inducements to moderation, nothing could be more ill-judged than that intolerant spirit which has, at

25   all times, characterized political parties. For in politics, as in religion, it is equally absurd to aim at making proselytes by fire and sword. Heresies in either can rarely be cured by persecution.

      And yet, however just these sentiments will be allowed to be, we have already sufficient indications that it will happen in this as in all former cases of great national discussion. A torrent of angry and malignant passions will be let loose. To judge from the conduct of the opposite

30   parties, we shall be led to conclude that they will mutually hope to evince the justness of their opinions, and to increase the number of their converts by the loudness of their declamations and the bitterness of their **calumnies**. An enlightened zeal for the energy and efficiency of government will be stigmatized as the offspring of a temper fond of despotic power and hostile to the principles of liberty. An over-scrupulous jealousy of danger to the rights of the people,

35   which is more commonly the fault of the head than of the heart, will be represented as mere

prevarication and artifice, the stale bait for popularity at the expense of the public good. It will be forgotten, on the one hand, that jealousy is the usual concomitant of love, and that the noble enthusiasm of liberty is apt to be infected with a spirit of narrow and illiberal distrust. On the other hand, it will be equally forgotten that the vigor of government is essential to the security

40 of liberty; that, in the contemplation of a sound and well-informed judgment, their interest can never be separated; and that a dangerous ambition more often lurks behind the specious mask of zeal for the rights of the people than under the forbidden appearance of zeal for the firmness and efficiency of government. History will teach us that the former has been found a much more certain road to the introduction of **despotism** than the latter, and that of those men

45 who have overturned the liberties of republics, the greatest number have begun their career by paying an obsequious court to the people; commencing demagogues, and ending tyrants.

In the course of the preceding observations, I have had an eye, my fellow-citizens, to putting you upon your guard against all attempts, from whatever quarter, to influence your decision in a matter of the utmost moment to your welfare, by any impressions other than those which may

50 result from the evidence of truth. You will, no doubt, at the same time, have collected from the general scope of them, that they proceed from a source not unfriendly to the new Constitution. Yes, my countrymen, I own to you that, after having given it an attentive consideration, I am clearly of opinion it is your interest to adopt it. I am convinced that this is the safest course for your liberty, your dignity, and your happiness. I affect not reserves which I do not feel. I will not

55 amuse you with an appearance of deliberation when I have decided. I frankly acknowledge to you my convictions, and I will freely lay before you the reasons on which they are founded. The consciousness of good intentions disdains ambiguity. I shall not, however, multiply professions on this head. My motives must remain in the depository of my own breast. My arguments will be open to all, and may be judged of by all. They shall at least be offered in a spirit which will not

60 disgrace the cause of truth.

1A. The goal of the new Constitution, as can be inferred from paragraph 1, is to
    A.   form small unions of states, which will answer to the central government.
    B.   reject any central government that attempts to rule over the states.
    C.   protect the rights of individuals within states.
    D.   unite the states under a single, central government.
    E.   reduce the power of states, and, thereby, eliminate corruption.

1B. Which line from paragraph 1 best supports your answer to question 1A?
    A.   "emolument and consequence of the offices they hold under the state"
    B.   "than from its union under one government"
    C.   "perverted ambition of another class of men"
    D.   "resist all changes which may hazard a diminution of the power"
    E.   "flatter themselves by filching fairer prospects"

2A. Hamilton claims that two types of people will be likely opponents to the new Constitution. One is characterized as fearful of losing power to the federal government. The other can be described as
    A.   favoring strong state governments over federal governments.
    B.   wishing for continued chaos, which they hope to use to their advantage.
    C.   enemies of change.
    D.   wanting to unite the states, but without a new Constitution.
    E.   eager to profit from deals made with the federal government.

2B. Choose the word in paragraph 1 that most nearly means, "to benefit."
    A.   aggrandize
    B.   diminution
    C.   elevation
    D.   hazard
    E.   subdivision

3A. According to paragraph 2, lines 11-17, which choice is *not* one of the reasons that good people might reject Hamilton's argument?
    A.   fear
    B.   candor
    C.   honest mistakes
    D.   false information
    E.   jealousy

3B. What approach does the author recommend to anyone tempted to argue his or her own personal beliefs?
    A.   repetition
    B.   zeal
    C.   avoidance
    D.   eloquence
    E.   moderation

4A. Which description of political parties would Hamilton agree with, according to paragraph 2?
    A.   Political parties tend to dismiss anyone who doesn't agree with their own tenets.
    B.   Political parties are the opposite of religion.
    C.   Political parties eagerly welcome people who aren't easily swayed.
    D.   Political parties are useless because they all believe the same thing.
    E.   Political parties tend to use moderation in defining their own beliefs.

4B. Choose the phrase from paragraph 2 that directly supports your answer to question 4A, as it appears in the context of political parties.
    A.   lesson of moderation
    B.   purer principles
    C.   personal animosity
    D.   ill-judged
    E.   intolerant spirit

5A. Which adage best mirrors the meaning of the following sentences from paragraph 2?

    "For in politics as in religion, it is equally absurd to aim at making proselytes by fire and sword. Heresies in either can rarely be cured by persecution."

    A.   You can lead a horse to water, but you can't make him drink.
    B.   It's a soldier's right to complain.
    C.   The beatings will continue until morale improves.
    D.   You'll catch more flies with honey than with vinegar.
    E.   Too many chefs spoil the recipe.

5B. By the way it is used in the context of line 26, the word *proselytes* most nearly means
   A.   friends.
   B.   rivals.
   C.   converts.
   D.   enemies.
   E.   connections.

6A. In paragraph 3, Hamilton warns that people who support the federal government will be "stigmatized" as power hungry (line 33), and "hostile to the principles of liberty." It is ironic, then, that he suggests that the same detractors of the Constitution might be
   A.   tyrants in waiting.
   B.   great orators.
   C.   supporters of liberty.
   D.   secret federalists.
   E.   saviors of the federal cause.

6B. Which choice best describes characteristics of leaders who should be regarded with suspicion, according to paragraph 3?
   A.   people who defend government as a means of ensuring rights
   B.   leaders who do not align with political parties
   C.   loud advocates of individual rights who curry favor with the public
   D.   people who argue that government works
   E.   leaders who are experts in world history

7A. The author explicitly states that he is
   A.   indifferent to the debate over the Constitution.
   B.   in favor of the Constitution.
   C.   opposed to uniting the states, for fear of a dictatorship.
   D.   an ardent supporter of a single political party.
   E.   against adoption of the Constitution.

7B. Choose the description of the author, from the choices below, which provides the best evidence for your answer to question 7A.
   A.   "I have had an eye…to putting you upon your guard"
   B.   "I own to you that, after having given it an attentive consideration"
   C.   "I affect not reserves which I do not feel"
   D.   "I frankly acknowledge to you my convictions"
   E.   "a source not unfriendly to the new Constitution"

8A. This passage is written for which audience?
   A.   the author's political party
   B.   citizens of the American states
   C.   leaders of the confederate states
   D.   supporters of the new Constitution
   E.   the new federal government formed by the Constitution

8B. The answer to question 8A can be determined from
    A. paragraph 1, in which the author refers to the government.
    B. paragraph 2, in which the author discusses moderation.
    C. paragraph 3, which describes the opposing sides of the debate.
    D. paragraph 4, where the author directly addresses citizens.
    E. paragraph 3, in the author's mention of tyrants.

9A. From the following choices, which would be the most appropriate, specific title for the essay?
    A. The Political Party Storm
    B. Tyrants After the Storm
    C. The Lighthouse in the Storm
    D. The Truth About the Storm
    E. The Storm Approaches

9B. All the titles provided in question 9A are metaphors. To which element of the essay does the word *storm* refer?
    A. the conflict of ideas as foretold by the author
    B. the political election season as established by the constitution
    C. the pending American War for Independence
    D. the time of chaos as America is divided into small confederacies
    E. the aftermath of the tyrant seizing control of the federal government

10A. This type of essay is best described as
    A. how-to.
    B. compare-contrast.
    C. biographical.
    D. argumentative.
    E. informational.

10B. Which of the following elements of the essay best supports your choice for the answer to question 10A?
    A. estimated numbers of supporters for the Constitution
    B. the author's explicit personal opinion
    C. facts about pending political conflicts
    D. instructions for getting information about the new Constitution
    E. descriptions of expected public reactions to conflict

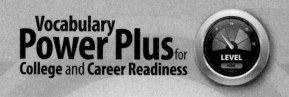

Lesson Eleven

1. **flagrant**   (flā´ grǝnt)   *adj.*   glaringly bad; outrageous
His *flagrant* disregard for authority caused the boy a lot of trouble.
syn: offensive; shameless; brazen

2. **patrician**   (pǝ trish´ ǝn)   *n.*   an aristocrat
The *patrician* could not marry the man she loved because he was a member of the working class.
syn: noble   *ant: commoner*

3. **emissary**   (em´ i sǝr ē)   *n.*   one sent on a special mission to represent others
Before the concept of diplomatic immunity, an *emissary* was often imprisoned or killed.
syn: ambassador; agent

4. **kindred**   (kin´ drid)   *adj.*   having a similar origin, nature, or character
They had met only days ago, but the two girls were *kindred* spirits and immediately became friends.
syn: homogeneous   *ant: disparate*

5. **fracas**   (frā´ kǝs)   *n.*   a loud quarrel or fight
The coaches broke up the *fracas* that began on the field during the game.
syn: brawl

6. **lacerate**   (las´ ǝ rāt)   *v.*   to tear (flesh) jaggedly
The pedal *lacerated* the rider's leg when the bicycle flipped over.
syn: slash; gash; rip   *ant: suture*

7. **futile**   (fyōōt´ ǝl, tl)   *adj.*   useless; pointless
I received a shock during my *futile* attempt to fix the television set.
syn: ineffectual; fruitless   *ant: effective; useful*

8. **immaculate**   (im mak´ yǝ lit)   *adj.*   spotless; perfect
The rooms of the mansion were as *immaculate* as the grounds surrounding the large estate.
syn: clean; pure   *ant: dirty; soiled; spotted*

9. **gait**   (gāt)   *n.*   the manner of walking
The horse's smooth *gait* made riding easy.
syn: walk

10. **carp** (kärp) *v.* to complain or find fault in a petty or nagging way
    No one wants to talk to you because you *carp* about every little thing.
    syn: grumble; nag; nitpick   *ant: praise; laud*

11. **query** (kwîr´ ē) *v.* to ask; to inquire
    The buyer decided to *query* the previous owners about the leaky plumbing before
    buying the house.
    syn: question; interrogate

12. **queue** (kyōō) *n.* a line of people or vehicles
    During the war, *queues* formed in front of butcher shops because meat was in short
    supply.

13. **nefarious** (nə fâr´ ē əs) *adj.* very wicked; notorious
    Billy the Kid was one of the most *nefarious* characters of the Old West.
    syn: villainous; despicable   *ant: reputable; honest*

14. **genesis** (jen´ ə sis) *n.* the beginning; origin
    The invention of the telegraph marked the *genesis* of the Information Age.
    syn: start; birth   *ant: conclusion; finish*

15. **façade** (fə säd´) *n.* a deceptive outward appearance; a misrepresentation
    Joan's cheerful *façade* did not hide her depression.
    syn: pretense; charade

Exercise I

Words in Context

From the list below, supply the words needed to complete the paragraph. Some words will not be used.

gait	futile	kindred	immaculate
emissary	query	nefarious	façade

1. When Cal took a job working at the docks, he didn't realize that he was going to become a[n] _____ for a[n] _____ businessman who made a fortune shipping black-market goods. After one week of unloading crates from ships and putting them on trucks during the graveyard shift, Cal _____ the supervisor as to the contents of the heavy wooden boxes. The question was _____; the supervisor just looked at Cal, paused for an uneasy moment, and then replied, "Tractor parts." At that moment, Cal realized that he was participating in a[n] _____ that concealed some type of illegal operation; even worse, he was a pawn for the businessman. If U.S. Customs was to raid the dock, Cal would probably be arrested while the boss's record remained _____.

From the list below, supply the words needed to complete the paragraph. Some words will not be used.

genesis	gait	emissary	queue
carp	patrician		

2. After six hours of driving, Charlie parked his car and walked across the parking lot with an odd _____. He was happy to stretch his legs, but he _____ about summer crowds when he saw that the _____ for the restroom extended around the corner of the rest stop. He should have expected as much, he reasoned; Memorial Day weekend was the traditional _____ of the summer season, and the crowds had arrived.

From the list below, supply the words needed to complete the paragraph. Some words will not be used.

flagrant	lacerate	fracas	immaculate
patrician	kindred	nefarious	

3. Most of the servants abandoned the grounds when they heard the _____ outside the front gates. A crowd of armed peasants gathered below, preparing to punish their _____ for what they described as a[n] _____ abuse of his title. Disease and famine were rampant throughout the villages of the manor, but Lord Geoffrey continued to raise taxes and host feasts for his _____ aristocrats. Nervously, Geoffrey peered from his chamber window to see his guards surrendering to the mob. The angry farmers and merchants did not _____ the guards with their sickles and poorly fashioned swords, but Geoffrey knew that they would not be so merciful with him. In a fit of panic, he began thinking of possible escape routes as the mob flooded into the courtyard through the gate.

Exercise II

Sentence Completion

Complete the sentence in a way that shows you understand the meaning of the italicized vocabulary word.

1. A *fracas* developed in the parking lot after...

2. Every day during work, the customer service representative had to listen to people *carp* about...

3. In American culture, it shows *flagrant* disrespect to...

4. The largely outnumbered army built hundreds of fires at night to create the *façade* that...

5. The *queue* at the ticket window was so long that Kim decided to...

6. The broken glass on the floor will *lacerate* your feet if you do not...

7. You should *query* the post office about the package if...

8. The officer suspected that something *nefarious* was occurring in the bank when he saw...

9. The photograph in the guide book showed an *immaculate* park, but the real park was...

10. Before the *genesis* of automobiles, people relied on...

11. The affluent *patrician* knew that his family would frown upon him for...

12. Despite their *kindred* roots, the two brothers...

13. Serena knew that if she didn't approach the podium with a confident *gait*, the audience would...

14. The United Nations sent an *emissary* to the poverty-stricken nation to...

15. Efforts to contain the floodwaters proved *futile* when...

Exercise III

Roots, Prefixes, and Suffixes

Study the entries and answer the questions that follow.

The root *am* means "friend" or "to love."
The root *aqu* means "water."
The root *brev* means "short."
The root *prot* means "first" or "original."

1. Using *literal* translations as guidance, define the following words without using a dictionary:

    A. amicable   D. aquatic
    B. amative   E. prototype
    C. aquarium   F. protagonist

2. If a word is long and you don't want to write it out, you might simply use its _____. If a speaker is known for her *brevity*, then her speeches must be _____.

3. Someone in a loving mood might be described as _____. That person might be in love with, or _____ of, someone else.

4. List as many words as you can think of that contain the roots *aqu* or *prot*.

Exercise IV

Inference

Complete the sentence by inferring information about the italicized word from its context.

1. If you *carp* about the decorations in your friend's new home, then your friend might not...

2. A criminal who is imprisoned for *nefarious* crimes must have done things that...

3. If a particular approach to solving a problem seems *futile*, then you should...

Exercise V

Writing

Here is a writing prompt similar to the one you will find on the writing portion of an assessment test.

Plan and write an essay based on the following statement:

> The farther backward you can look, the farther forward you are likely to see.
> –Sir Winston Churchill

Assignment: In an essay, rephrase Churchill's statement and explain whether you agree or disagree with it. Does the assertion apply to all humanity or only individuals? Does it apply to the present time or just certain periods in history? Support your essay with evidence from your own reading, classroom studies, experiences, and observations.

Thesis: Write a *one-sentence* response to the assignment. Make certain this single sentence offers a clear statement of your position.

Example: According to Sir Winston Churchill, history repeats itself, and a good memory is the best tool for predicting the future.

_____

_____

Organizational Plan: List at least three subtopics you will use to support your main idea. This list is your outline.

1. _____

2. _____

3. _____

Draft: Following your outline, write a good first draft of your essay. Remember to support all your points with examples, facts, references to reading, etc.

Review and Revise: Exchange essays with a classmate. Using the scoring guide for Organization on page 251, score your partner's essay (while he or she scores yours). Focus on the organizational plan and the use of language conventions. If necessary, rewrite your essay to improve the organizational plan and/or your use of language.

Exercise VI

Improving Paragraphs

Read the following passage and then answer the multiple-choice questions that follow. The questions will require you to make decisions regarding the revision of the reading selection.

1   (1) While riding on a roller coaster moving 70 miles per hour, you probably need to squint your eyes to see, or they well up with tears. (2) Your hair and your shirt flap in the wind like streamers, and your hat, if you wore one, have long departed.

2   (3) Now imagine that you are in free fall, 5000 feet above the surface of the earth, and you have just reached a terminal velocity of 120 miles per hour. (4) Seeing anything without goggles is impossible, and the material of your jumpsuit flaps so quickly that it makes a buzzing sound. (5) Now picture yourself in the cockpit of a fighter jet that's plummeting toward Earth at 800 miles per hour, faster than sound, and faster than some bullets. (6) You're at 10,000 feet, and the aircraft is out of control. (7) If you stay with the plane, you will die in seconds. (8) If you eject, you might be killed instantly. (9) Unimaginable? (10) Not for Captain Brian Udell.

3   (11) During a nighttime Air Force training sortie off the coast of North Carolina, the instruments in Captain Udell's F-15E Strike Eagle malfunctioned. (12) One set told him everything was fine, while the other suggested an impending disaster. (13) The heads-up display indicated that his flight status was normal, but, according to other (functioning) indicators, his jet was plummeting straight to Earth at nearly supersonic speed. (14) In little more than a second, Udell gave Dennis White, the weapons system officer, the order to bail out, and by the time the canopy blew at 5,000 feet, the jet had accelerated to over 780 miles per hour—1,200 feet per second.

4   (15) Udell's ACES II ejection seat cleared the aircraft at 3,000 feet above the ocean. (16) Air resistance at Mach 1 **lacerated** Udell as he slowed to subsonic speeds, but luckily, his chute functioned and caught the air at less than 1,000 feet, had he hesitated just one half-second longer, the chute would not have deployed in time, and the impact on the water would have killed him.

5   (17) Don't ask Udell what is was like to travel at Mach 1 without the luxury of a plane; he is glad to have no memory of the three seconds that followed the pull of the ejection lever. (18) He recollects only his descent to the water, pulling his broken body into a waterlogged raft and then discovering how the ejection had battered his body. (19) His mask and helmet had been stripped from his head, and anything he had in his pockets had torn through. (20) His flight suit was shredded, and the skin of his face was stretched and swollen. (21) His arm and ankle were dislocated, his rib was cracked, and the tendons in his right knee were so damaged that his lower leg flopped uselessly onto his other leg when he flipped it into the raft. (22) The injuries were substantial, but the price was relatively small; Captain White, the weapons officer, did not survive the ejection. (23) It was **futile** to paddle, so Udell waited alone, cold and broken in the dark water, for four hours before the Coast Guard located him. (24) Two months and several surgeries after the unfortunate night, Brian Udell walked again with a painful **gait**. (25) Eight months later, Udell was back in the cockpit, but the lifelong pilot (he learned to fly when he was nine) had a different perspective of his aviation career: it would always be second to the family he almost left behind.

1.   Which of the following suggestions corrects the error in sentence 2?
    A.   Replace *you* with *one would*.
    B.   Replace *have* with *has*.
    C.   Replace *flap* with *flaps*.
    D.   Form two sentences from sentence 1.
    E.   Combine both sentences.

2. Which of the following changes to paragraph 2 would improve the flow of the passage?
   A. Delete *Unimaginable*.
   B. Combine sentences 3 and 4.
   C. Insert a comma after *flaps*.
   D. Begin a new paragraph after sentence 4.
   E. Replace *You're* with *Your*.

3. Which unnecessary sentence should be deleted from paragraph 3?
   A. Sentence 11
   B. Sentence 12
   C. Sentence 13
   D. Sentence 14
   E. Sentences 11 and 14

4. Which suggestion would correct a grammatical error in paragraph 4?
   A. Put a period after *1000 feet* and capitalize *had*.
   B. Change *ACES* to lowercase letters.
   C. Replace *killed* with *hurt*.
   D. Combine sentences 15 and 16.
   E. Place a comma after *hesitated*.

5. What would best conclude the passage?
   A. Replace the semicolon after *small* with a period.
   B. In one more paragraph, compare Udell's experience to that of an automobile race.
   C. Include a paragraph about Udell's family.
   D. Begin a new paragraph after *pockets had torn through*.
   E. Begin a new paragraph after *Coast Guard located him*.

Lesson Twelve

1. **deluge** (del´ yōōj) *n.* a flood; an overwhelming rush
    The new amusement park experienced a *deluge* of visitors on opening day.
    syn: inundation; surge   *ant: drought; dearth*

2. **catholic** (kath´ lik) *adj.* universal; wide-ranging
    His *catholic* interests made him quite knowledgeable in many subjects.
    syn: broad   *ant: provincial; limited; parochial*

3. **eerie** (îr´ ē) *adj.* weird; mysterious; strange and frightening
    No one accepted the dare to stay in the *eerie* old mansion for one night.
    syn: sinister; creepy   *ant: common; ordinary*

4. **martial** (mär´ shəl) *adj.* warlike; relating to the military
    A state of *martial* law was declared in the small country in the weeks following the
    overthrow of the government.

5. **anthropomorphic** (an´ thrə pə môrf´ ik) *adj.* attributing human
         characteristics or qualities to objects, animals, or gods
    Anthropomorphic stories might feature pigs and rabbits walking upright, wearing
    clothes, and speaking to each other in human languages.

6. **beneficiary** (ben ə fish´ ē er ē) *n.* one who receives benefits
    John was the sole *beneficiary* of his Uncle Martin's vast estate.
    syn: recipient; heir

7. **careen** (kə rēn´) *v.* to swerve or lurch from side to side while in motion
    The torrential winds caused the ship to *careen* violently.
    syn: tilt

8. **aplomb** (ə pläm´) *n.* self-confidence
    The *aplomb* of the young dancer astonished the veterans of the troupe.
    syn: assurance; poise   *ant: awkwardness*

9. **guile** (gīl) *n.* slyness and cunning in dealing with others
    Brad's *guile* contributed to his wealth, but it also created enemies.
    syn: craftiness; astuteness   *ant: honesty*

10. **modicum** (mod´ i kəm) *n.* a small amount
    A sudden shower gave us a *modicum* of relief from the heat and humidity.
    syn: bit   *ant: abundance*

11. **fester** (fes′ tər)   *v.*   to grow worse over time; to rot
    If allowed to *fester*, dislike can turn into bitter hatred.
    syn: aggravate; worsen

12. **languish** (lan′ gwish)   *v.*   to become weak or feeble; to lose strength
    The bill *languished* in Congress for nearly ten years.
    syn: wither; fade   *ant: thrive; flourish*

13. **pall** (pôl)   *n.*   something that covers or conceals
    A *pall* of gloom descended over the crowd.
    syn: shroud

14. **havoc** (hav′ ək)   *n.*   great destruction; chaos
    The commandos wreaked *havoc* throughout the area when they infiltrated the secret base.
    syn: mayhem; disorder   *ant: order*

15. **rancid** (ran′ sid)   *adj.*   having a bad taste or smell; spoiled
    The bitter fight over child custody left a *rancid* taste in both lawyers' mouths.
    syn: rotten; repulsive   *ant: fresh*

Exercise I

Words in Context

From the list below, supply the words needed to complete the paragraph. Some words will not be used.

deluge	pall	career	fester
modicum	martial	beneficiary	

1.   Everyone anticipated the opening of the new state park, but not the strict, almost
     _____ rules and prohibitions that imposed fines for camping, cooking,
     swimming, or walking in unauthorized areas. Immediately after the park opened, the
     Department of Parks and Recreation received a _____ of letters questioning
     who, exactly, the _____ of the new park were supposed to be, since the people
     who paid for the park apparently were not. Without at least a _____ of freedom
     to explore the old forest, people complained, the park was simply private property.
     Most agreed that the park would be wonderful without the _____ of restrictions
     hanging over it.

From the list below, supply the words needed to complete the paragraph. Some words will not be used.

fester	aplomb	guile	havoc
languish	rancid	pall	

2.   The power outage brought _____ to the meat processing plant. For hours,
     workers _____ in the dark struggling to move tons of perishable food to
     refrigerated trailers before it began to _____ in the rapidly warming warehouse.
     Any meat left in the facility after a designated time was declared _____ and
     marked for disposal. Many workers worried about the fate of the company, but the
     owner reassured them and asked them with _____ to keep their composure
     through the crisis.

From the list below, supply the words needed to complete the paragraph. Some words will not be used.

catholic	eerie	martial	anthropomorphic
guile	rancid	career	

3.   The children's book features _____ animal characters that speak and interact as
     though they are people. In the story, a sneaky wolf uses his _____ to manipulate
     a chicken into leaving its pen and entering the _____ old forest behind the farm.
     The wolf, of course, then tries to eat the chicken, but the chicken _____ around
     rocks and trees, causing the wolf to become dizzy and give up the chase. Like many
     children's books, this one has _____ themes that appeal to all audiences.

Exercise II

Sentence Completion

Complete the sentence in a way that shows you understand the meaning of the italicized vocabulary word.

1. The engineers exhibited great *aplomb* during the reactor meltdown, but...

2. Eric expected to find *eerie* paintings hanging on the walls when he...

3. Marjorie did not want to *languish* in the hot sun, so she...

4. She knew that the milk was *rancid* because...

5. The producers wanted the new sitcom to be *catholic* enough to...

6. Renee has the *guile* to become...

7. Sandy thought the rules in her new school seemed almost *martial* because...

8. In the *anthropomorphic* cartoon, the animals...

9. Randy wanted only a *modicum* of silence after a long day of...

10. A *deluge* of customers swamped the store on the day that...

11. Tim was Howard's *beneficiary*, so when Howard died, Tim...

12. The potato salad will *fester* in the sun, so you should...

13. Foods that wreak *havoc* on your teeth include...

14. The smog created a *pall* that...

15. The car *careened* all over the highway when the driver...

Exercise III

Roots, Prefixes, and Suffixes

Study the entries and answer the questions that follow.

The roots *patr* and *patern* mean "father."
The root *scop* means "to watch."
The roots *scrib* and *script* mean "to write."
The root *cent* means "one hundred."

1. Using *literal* translations as guidance, define the following words without using a dictionary:

   A. manuscript   D. centennial
   B. scripture   E. percent
   C. scribe   F. horoscope

2. To see things far away, you might watch them through a[n] _____, but to see tiny things, you might use a[n] _____.

3. *Arch* means "ruler," so a male leader of a family is called a[n] _____. If you talk down to someone as though you were the father and he were the child, you are said to _____ that person. A _____ test can verify that someone is the father of a child.

4. List as many words as you can think of that contain the roots *scrib* or *script*.

Exercise IV

Inference

Complete the sentence by inferring information about the italicized word from its context.

1. You are the *beneficiary* on my insurance policy, so if anything happens to me, you will…

2. *Anthropomorphic* animals in literature might speak English, drive cars, or do anything that makes them…

3. Only a *modicum* of readers claimed to dislike the…

Exercise V

Critical Reading

Below is a pair of reading passages followed by several multiple-choice questions. Carefully read the passages and choose the best answer for each of the questions.

The following passages discuss parts of women's suffrage. The first passage focuses on famous suffragettes. The second passage describes barriers that the suffragettes had to overcome.

Passage 1

Women have been fighting for equal rights since the middle of the nineteenth century. While some women argue that they still do not have equal rights, they cannot argue that the cause has not come a long way since Elizabeth Cady Stanton and Susan B. Anthony took the first steps toward the acceptance of women's suffrage.

5   Elizabeth Cady Stanton was a pioneer for women's rights. At her own wedding, she appalled her guests by intentionally omitting the word "obey" while reciting her vows; fortunately, her husband supported her view that women are equal to men. Driven by her cause, Stanton—a mother of seven children—made time to become a leading activist for the rights of women. She wrote speeches for Susan B. Anthony, she spoke at numerous women's rights
10   conventions, and, using the Declaration of Independence for inspiration, she drafted the 1848 Seneca Falls declaration. New Englanders were moved by the powerful rhetoric in her speeches. She believed that women were morally superior and, therefore, deserved the right to participate in politics.

    Susan B. Anthony, born in Massachusetts, was also a pioneer in the women's rights
15   arena. While a young schoolgirl, Anthony questioned her teacher as to why he taught long division only to boys. He explained that women did not need to know how to do long division—only how to read a Bible and run a home. Anthony then took it upon herself to learn long division by listening in on the teacher's long-division lessons to the boys. Anthony became so prominent as a women's rights advocate that women who joined the cause
20   were called "Susie Bs." One of Anthony's defining moments came when she, along with a few other women, registered to vote during the election of 1871. Fifteen women actually succeeded in voting, and though they were later arrested and fined, they did not fail in making history.

    If it were not for these forerunners who challenged the **pall** of inequity over women,
25   women's rights would be nowhere near where they are today. These difficult strides have secured a nation in which women, the **beneficiaries**, are free to earn a living, govern states, or run for president. Elizabeth Cady Stanton and Susan B. Anthony deserve thanks for over a century of progress, and many women look to them as role models and inspiration.

Passage 2

Many who are aware of the women's suffrage movement are not aware of the depths of the opposition that tried to quash the effort. Many wise, brave women worked hard in the quest for rights, but there were even more men who fought against them. The anti-suffragists maintained several reasons for their resistance, from questions of morality to the physical limitations of
5   women. In the present, most of the reasons would be dismissed as silly, but in the nineteenth century, they were considerable roadblocks to women's suffrage.

    Physical limitation of women was a significant part of the anti-suffragist platform, and some men still regard it as a legitimate concern. Women, according to men in the nineteenth century, lacked the capacity to make important decisions or even the physical

10   stamina to actually make the decisions. A number of men proposed that women would be so
       physically exhausted by making the trip to the poll that they would be too disoriented to make
       intelligent choices! A woman's emotional instability, the men also argued, affected her ability
       to reason, thus disqualifying her from voting.

           Some challengers claimed that it would have been immoral to allow women to vote.
15   Drawing on the Bible's Book of Genesis, some men maintained the theory that once Eve gained
       wisdom from the tree of knowledge, **havoc ensued**; if women were to get what they wanted—
       voting rights—everything would go farther downhill. Other men suggested that women who
       wore long sleeves would be compelled to cheat by concealing extra ballots and voting more
       than once; apparently, it never occurred to the men that they were able to do the same thing
20   when they wore long sleeves!

           Perhaps the most shocking anti-suffragist tactic was to describe women's suffrage as a har-
       binger of the destruction of the traditional family structure. They warned that women would
       lose their feminine qualities if they assumed male responsibilities such as voting. In reaction to
       the shifting gender roles, men would **languish** and become effeminate. Once these roles were
25   corrupted, the entire family would suffer and eventually fall apart.

           Most of the anti-suffragist arguments lacked any plausible evidence to support them; they
       were simply cries of desperation in the face of great changes in the world. Some of the other
       prophecies have been realized, but through the decades, society has come to understand them
       not as negative consequences, necessarily, but as products of an advancing civilization. Gender
30   roles have indeed changed since the birth of the women's rights movement, and the traditional
       family is also changing. Women's suffrage was, without a doubt, a crucial step in human prog-
       ress, but like any great change, it had advocates and adversaries.

1A. The purpose of passage 1 is to
     A.   inform readers about women's suffrage.
     B.   persuade people that Elizabeth Stanton was a pioneer for women's rights.
     C.   entertain an audience with historical facts.
     D.   challenge a notion that Elizabeth Stanton failed.
     E.   laud the work of Susan B. Anthony.

1B. Which type of evidence from passage 1 best supports your answer to question 1A?
     A.   personal opinion about the most important suffragette
     B.   historical facts about the chronology of women's suffrage
     C.   excessive details about personal virtues
     D.   the rebuking of erroneous historians
     E.   arguments against contrary historical data

2A. Which of the following is *not* a way in which Stanton, as a leading activist, directly
     helped the cause of women's suffrage?
     A.   leaving out "obey" from wedding vows
     B.   writing speeches for Anthony
     C.   drafting the Seneca Falls declaration
     D.   speaking at women's rights conventions
     E.   using her powerful rhetoric

2B. Which statement is probably *false* about Stanton, according to passage 1, paragraph 2?
     A.   She thought women were more considerate of others than men were.
     B.   She was an effective speaker.
     C.   She advocated the principles of the founding of the United States.
     D.   She was willing to shock her opponents with unexpected behavior.
     E.   She refused to be part of a traditional family.

3A. As used in line 11 of the first passage, *rhetoric* most nearly means
    A.   speaking.
    B.   style of speaking.
    C.   the study of principles and rules of composition.
    D.   knowledge.
    E.   a type of language.

3B. Because of Stanton's historical era and the nature of her cause, one can infer that her writing and speeches had to
    A.   convince only women to fight for equal rights.
    B.   address the importance of careers.
    C.   convince people that she was not trying to eliminate families.
    D.   gain the support of both women and men.
    E.   contain specific directions on what needed to be done.

4A. Which of the following is evidence of Anthony's widespread influence?
    A.   She taught herself long division.
    B.   Women who followed her were called "Susie Bs."
    C.   She registered to vote.
    D.   Fifteen women voted.
    E.   She was arrested for her activities.

4B. From the answer to question 4A, it can be inferred that Susan B. Anthony was successful in
    A.   avoiding arrest.
    B.   establishing voting rights for all women.
    C.   teaching math to women.
    D.   educating herself in spite of scholastic bias against women.
    E.   recruiting like-minded supporters.

5A. In line 7 of the second passage, *platform* means
    A.   theater stage.
    B.   declaration of principles.
    C.   elevated perspective.
    D.   place to speak.
    E.   common ground.

5B. Which choice is *not* a concern of the anti-suffragists described in passage 2?
    A.   moral tradition
    B.   economic consequences
    C.   voter fraud
    D.   risk to traditional family structure
    E.   control over emotions

6A. According to the second passage, which was *not* a potential effect on family life if women were granted suffrage?
    A.   Women would assume male responsibilities.
    B.   Women would lose their feminine qualities.
    C.   Masculinity would become obsolete.
    D.   Men would become effeminate.
    E.   The family would fall apart.

6B. Which choice is the most specific description of the main subject of passage 2?
    A.   the history of women's suffrage
    B.   women's suffrage today
    C.   moral implication of women's suffrage
    D.   obstacles to women's suffrage
    E.   women's rights

7A. As used in line 21 of the second passage, *harbinger* most nearly means
    A.   an attack.
    B.   a bringer.
    C.   a result.
    D.   a deletion.
    E.   a message.

7B. Which word from the context of *harbinger* best supports your answer to question 7A?
    A.   corrupted
    B.   destruction
    C.   warned
    D.   suffer
    E.   compelled

8A. Which of the following is one of the products of an advancing civilization, according to the second passage?
    A.   Women cheat by voting twice.
    B.   Traditional family roles change.
    C.   Women grow emotionally stable.
    D.   People vote electronically.
    E.   Men cease voting.

8B. What does passage 2 include that passage 1 omits?
    A.   social commentary on gender and family
    B.   examples of resistance to changes in equality
    C.   positive opinions of women's rights
    D.   belief in the ineffectiveness of suffrage
    E.   details of early women's rights efforts

9A. The overall tone of passage 2 is
  A. severely critical.
  B. speculative.
  C. mildly ironic.
  D. apathetic.
  E. condemning.

9B. Which element in passage 2 best supports your answer to question 9A?
  A. specific details about women's suffrage events and milestones
  B. statements from historians alive during equal rights campaigns
  C. exclamations of details that might contradict modern belief
  D. inclusion of negative consequences of women's suffrage
  E. the total lack of personal opinion about suffrage

10A. The authors of both passages would probably agree that
  A. women should play the major role in politics.
  B. individuals can make more of a difference than groups can.
  C. some women earned the right to vote, but others do not deserve it.
  D. the right to vote is precious.
  E. gender roles will always be different for men and women.

10B. Both passages portray the women's suffrage movement as
  A. positive and necessary.
  B. arduous and ongoing.
  C. senseless and futile.
  D. risky and luck-driven.
  E. historic and ineffective.

Exercise I

Inferences

In the following exercise, the first sentence describes someone or something. Infer information from the first sentence, and then choose the word from the Word Bank that best completes the second sentence.

neophyte	calumny	gait	kindred
lacerate	aplomb	languish	immaculate

1. Just out of law school, the young lawyer strolled into her new firm like she owned the place, even calling the senior partners by their first names.

   From this sentence, we can infer that the lawyer has no shortage of _____.

2. The strangers became great friends when they learned that they shared the same hobbies, interests, and attitudes.

   From this sentence, we can infer that their _____ interests helped the friends get along well.

3. The crash was attributed to the young pilot's inexperience; he had received his license only a week before.

   From this sentence, we can infer that the pilot was an aviation _____.

4. Because it was rarely allowed out of its tiny cage, the rabbit became weak and sickly.

   From this sentence, we can infer that the rabbit _____ in captivity.

5. A shrapnel wound to his knee caused the old combat soldier to walk with a limp.

   From this sentence, we can infer that the injury changed the veteran's _____.

Exercise II

Related Words

Some of the vocabulary words from Lessons 10 through 12 have related meanings. Complete the following sentences by choosing the word that best fits the context, based on information you infer from the use of the italicized word. Some word pairs will be antonyms, some will be synonyms, and some will simply be words often used in the same context.

1. Devon's talent for *guile* helps him sell his herbal energy supplements; he has to
    _____ about the benefits of the pills since they are nothing more than sugar
    and caffeine.
    A. lacerate
    B. carp
    C. prevaricate
    D. imbibe
    E. berate

2. The inmate donned a stolen guard uniform, slipped into line behind the officers
    leaving at the end of their shift, and then strolled with _____ toward the front
    gate before anyone noticed the *façade*.
    A. bane
    B. genesis
    C. modicum
    D. kindred
    E. aplomb

3. Stranded deep in the desert, the survivors did not *dawdle* around the vehicle
    very long because they knew they would _____ beneath the relentless sun
    soon enough.
    A. languish
    B. obtrude
    C. fawn
    D. pacify
    E. careen

4. Each mistake on the field reminded the *neophyte* that she was in the _____ of
    her career and that she had years of learning ahead of her.
    A. pall
    B. despot
    C. gait
    D. genesis
    E. bane

5. Mrs. Stork had always kept a[n] _____ home, so it shocked her friends to learn that she had become a hoarder and surrounded herself with cats, piles of old newspapers, and containers of *rancid* food that had expired years ago.
   A. eerie
   B. kindred
   C. immaculate
   D. desolate
   E. primeval

6. Dr. Insano's *nefarious* henchmen created _____ throughout the city, raiding jewelry stores, stealing buses, and running over fire hydrants.
   A. modicum
   B. calumny
   C. beneficiary
   D. neophyte
   E. havoc

7. The governor declared _____ law in the city and ordered the troops to *pacify* Dr. Insano's rioters, who were now looting and setting fires.
   A. blatant
   B. catholic
   C. composite
   D. martial
   E. nefarious

8. The ugly rumor cast a _____ over the treasurer's reputation, and he spent years tracking down the source of the *calumny*.
   A. gait
   B. pall
   C. deluge
   D. forum
   E. guile

9. Kendy is the only oboe player in the band, so it was *futile* for her to pretend that she had not just made a[n] _____ mistake during the concert.
   A. undue
   B. blatant
   C. fallible
   D. nefarious
   E. flagrant

10. Subjects in the duke's territory respected their *patrician*, as they were the _____ of his modest tax rate and his fair decisions in court.
    A. beneficiaries
    B. ingrates
    C. neophytes
    D. queues
    E. emissaries

Exercise III

Deeper Meanings

Choose a word to replace the italicized word in each sentence. All of the possible choices for each sentence have similar definitions, but the correct answer will have a connotation that best suits the context. For example, the words "delete," "destroy," and "obliterate" all mean "to remove or wipe out," but no one would ever say, "I destroyed the name from the document." The correct choice will be the word that has the best specific meaning and does not render the sentence awkward in tone or content. When choices seem close, look for a clue in the context that makes one choice better than the other.

Note that the correct answer is not always the primary vocabulary word from the lesson.

calumny	havoc	perfect	odd
flagrant	problems	immaculate	accusation
disturbing	daring	disarray	tidy

1. Cash spilling from the rear of an armored truck, unbeknownst to the driver, caused *trouble* on the four-lane highway as cars screeched to a halt and scavengers risked their lives to grab fistfuls of money from the pavement.

   Better word: _____

2. To prevent the contamination of experiments, the staff ensures that the laboratory is *clean*, because a single speck of dust or a bacteria germ is all it takes to throw off their data.

   Better word: _____

3. Using the donations for the children's shelter to pay for a Hawaiian vacation was a[n] *inconsiderate* abuse of the charity director's authority.

   Better word: _____

4. The treasurer's career spiraled downward after his rival's *rumor* against him made national news, even though the disgraceful accusation was completely fabricated.

   Better word: _____

5. Beatrice thought it was *eerie* that the grocery store was completely out of skim milk and bread.

   Better word: _____

Exercise IV

Crossword Puzzle

Use the clues to complete the crossword puzzle. The answers consist of vocabulary words from Lessons 10 through 12.

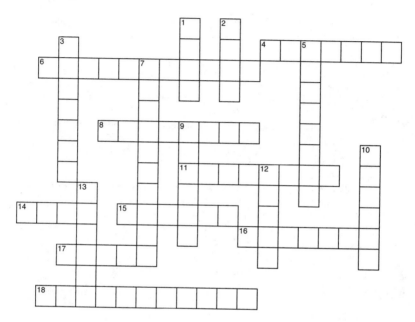

Across
4. bad-talk
6. receiver
8. worse than bad
11. rookie
14. enemy
15. take the fight out of
16. just a little bit
17. stand here with these people
18. tell a tall tale

Down
1. It's a walk, not part of a fence.
2. whine about
3. the beginning of everything
5. slice up
7. super clean
9. expired milk characteristic
10. "I can do anything"
12. total chaos
13. big flood

Exercise V

Subject Prompts

Here is a writing prompt similar to the one you will find on the writing portion of an assessment test. Follow the instructions below and write a brief, efficient essay.

> Building a nation is a centuries-long process, but it begins with a solid foundation of rules or rights that will influence or dictate the nation's growth, shape, and political dynamics.
>
> Imagine that you have just founded your very own nation in a geographic region of your choosing. The first order of business, and your assignment, is to write a constitution, or a charter, that details what your government can and cannot do in your nation (a dictatorship is not an option). Your first constitution will deal with generalities such as rights—not specific laws on personal behavior.
>
> Think of the top three principles that you would include in your constitution and explain why each one is necessary and important. Your points should be specific, i.e., no "everyone will be nice to each other." Remember to include an introduction and conclusion to your argument. Support your topic with examples, stories, or your own ideas and observations. Be sure to explain why each of your subtopics is essential to your nation, and how, or if, they are linked to one another.

Thesis: Write a *one-sentence* response to the above assignment. Make certain this single sentence offers a clear statement of your position.

Example: The primary right of all the citizens in my nation will be that they pay taxes only for the services that they need or use.

_____

_____

Organizational Plan: List at least three subtopics you will use to support your main idea. This list is your outline.

1. _____

2. _____

3. _____

Draft: Following your outline, write a good first draft of your essay. Remember to support all your points with examples, facts, references to reading, etc.

Review and Revise: Exchange essays with a classmate. Using the scoring guide for Word Choice on page 255, score your partner's essay (while he or she scores yours). Focus on word choice and the use of language conventions. If necessary, rewrite your essay to improve word choice and/or your use of language.

Lesson Thirteen

1. **holocaust** (hol' ə kôst) *n.* a great or complete destruction of life
Many feared that the Cuban Missile Crisis was going to end in a nuclear *holocaust.*

2. **embroil** (em broil') *v.* to draw into a conflict or fight
The new zoning ordinance *embroiled* members of the planning committee.
syn: entangle

3. **anachronism** (a nak' rə nizm) *n.* something existing outside of its
proper time
Some consider the use of fossil fuels to be an *anachronism* in this age of
nuclear technology.

4. **denigrate** (den' i grāt) *v.* to attack the reputation of; to speak ill of
The senator, who opposed political mudslinging, refused to *denigrate* his opponent.
syn: defame; belittle   *ant: praise; promote*

5. **humane** (hyōō mān') *adj.* kind; compassionate
Putting the critically injured horse out of its misery is the most *humane* course
of action.
syn: kindly; benevolent; considerate   *ant: inhumane; cruel*

6. **effusive** (i fyōō' siv) *adj.* emotionally excessive; overly demonstrative
I don't argue with you in public because your *effusive* responses embarrass me.
syn: gushing   *ant: reserved; restrained*

7. **defunct** (di fungkt') *adj.* no longer in existence
Don't get scammed into buying stock in a *defunct* corporation.
syn: invalid; extinct

8. **lackey** (lak' ē) *n.* a slavish follower
I want to speak to the boss, not a *lackey* who screens visitors for him.
syn: minion

9. **envisage** (en viz' ij, vis) *v.* to form a mental picture
You should *envisage* the task before you begin it.
syn: imagine; visualize

10. **lament** (lə ment') *v.* to mourn
Devoted fans *lamented* the death of the popular singer.
syn: grieve   *ant: rejoice*

11. **gape** (gāp) *v.* to stare with an open mouth
The child *gaped* at his mother in astonishment when she switched off the television.

12. **impertinent** (im pûr´ tə nənt) *adj.* rude and disrespectful
The boy earned an after-school detention for his *impertinent* behavior.
syn: insolent; impolite　　　　　　　　　*ant: polite; courteous*

13. **lofty** (lôf´ tē) *adj.* superior in style or tone; distinguished
The new boss brought *lofty* goals that struck most of the workers as impossible.
syn: elevated; imposing　　　　　　　　*ant: modest*

14. **nemesis** (nem´ i sis) *n.* someone or something a person cannot conquer or achieve; a hated enemy
Sherlock Holmes tried to outwit his *nemesis*, Moriarty.
syn: rival; adversary　　　　　　　　*ant: collaborator; friend*

15. **lethal** (lē´ thəl) *adj.* deadly; fatal
The clean-up crew wore respirators to protect themselves from the *lethal* vapors.
syn: mortal　　　　　　　　　*ant: harmless*

Exercise I

Words in Context

From the list below, supply the words needed to complete the paragraph. Some words will not be used.

lethal	**effusive**	**gape**	**anachronism**
holocaust	**defunct**	**embroil**	

1. The argument over the reality of global warming _____ many scientists, most of whom disagree among themselves. Some claim that global warming will cause a planetary _____ in which nothing will survive. Other scientists claim such _____ theories are meant only to cause worldwide panic. Indeed, they agree that global warming exists, but that it might take thousands of years to cause the climate to become _____. In a thousand years, or even a hundred years, they assert, the processes that cause global warming will be made _____ by new technologies.

From the list below, supply the words needed to complete the paragraph. Some words will not be used.

lackey	**denigrate**	**lament**	**anachronism**
nemesis	**defunct**	**humane**	

2. Old Carl knew that he was a[n] _____ amid the young programmers working in his office. Each time he struggled to send a simple e-mail, he _____ the death of the typewriter-and-telephone era in which he had spent most of his career. Bitter that the end of his own usefulness approached, Carl often _____ the young programmers for having no concept of how to use their own brains—not calculators—to solve equations or analyze data. Technology had become the programmer's _____, he felt, and had turned him into a dinosaur. Sometimes the young manager and his _____ mused at Carl's outdated experience with punch cards and mainframes, and it fueled Carl's resentment. He couldn't wait to retire.

From the list below, supply the words needed to complete the paragraph. Some words will not be used.

gape	**envisage**	**humane**	**impertinent**
holocaust	**lofty**	**lackey**	

3. "You know that it's _____ to stare and make faces," said the nanny in a[n] _____ tone. "_____ yourself in the same situation. How would you feel if every child who passed _____ at you as though you were a sideshow attraction? Learn to be a little more _____ toward your fellow man."

Exercise II

Sentence Completion

Complete the sentence in a way that shows you understand the meaning of the italicized vocabulary word.

1. George *denigrated* Suzanne by spreading rumors that she…

2. Pat *gaped* when she saw…

3. The character's cell phone was an *anachronism* in the movie because…

4. The famous actor traveled with a group of *lackeys* who…

5. The politician's *lofty* speech left everyone thinking…

6. Since my car's manufacturer is now *defunct*, I cannot get…

7. During dinner, it's *impertinent* for you to…

8. The representative at the travel agency said, "*Envisage* yourself…

9. Greg became Aaron's *nemesis* when he…

10. The entire community *lamented* the…

11. When the *effusive* man found a bogus charge on his telephone bill, he…

12. The huge hurricane was a natural *holocaust* that…

13. It is not *humane* to leave your…

14. The devious businessman spread rumors that *embroiled* his…

15. The doctor reassured the patient that the substance she encountered was not *lethal* and that she would…

Exercise III

Roots, Prefixes, and Suffixes

Study the entries and answer the questions that follow.

The roots *pot* and *poss* mean "to be able."
The prefix *psych–* means "mind."
The root *arm* means "tools" or "arms" (weapons).

1. Using *literal* translations as guidance, define the following words without using a dictionary:

    A. potential   D. psychology
    B. potent   E. alarm
    C. psyche   F. disarm

2. If no one can make the journey, it is said to be _____. An *impotent* worker is _____ to do a good job.

3. List as many words as you can think of that contain the roots *poss*, *pot*, or *arm*.

Exercise IV

Inference

Complete the sentence by inferring information about the italicized word from its context.

1. The former teacher preferred to *denigrate* her students rather than…

2. If high tariffs on all goods *embroil* the colonists with the mother country, the colonists might…

3. Since the cave contained *lethal* amounts of poison gas, the rescuers had to…

Exercise V

Writing

Here is a writing prompt similar to the one you will find on the writing portion of an assessment test.

Plan and write an essay based on the following statement:

> The world is a dangerous place, not because of those who do evil,
> but because of those who look on and do nothing.
>
> –Albert Einstein

Assignment: In an essay, indicate whether you agree or disagree with Albert Einstein's assertion about the origins of danger in the world. Is the world more dangerous because of evil-doers or because of people who take no action? Support your opinion using evidence from history, current events, literature, or your experience.

Thesis: Write a *one-sentence* response to the assignment. Make certain this single sentence offers a clear statement of your position.

Example: Albert Einstein's idea that indifferent people are responsible for the dangers in the world is correct because the world will always have evil people, and the only way to stop them is for everyone else to take action.

_____

_____

Organizational Plan: List at least three subtopics you will use to support your main idea. This list is your outline.

1. _____

2. _____

3. _____

Draft: Following your outline, write a good first draft of your essay. Remember to support all your points with examples, facts, references to reading, etc.

Review and Revise: Exchange essays with a classmate. Using the scoring guide for Development on page 252, score your partner's essay (while he or she scores yours). Focus on the development of ideas and the use of language conventions. If necessary, rewrite your essay to incorporate more (or more relevant) support and/or improve your use of language.

Exercise VI

English Practice

Identifying Sentence Errors

Identify the grammatical error in each of the following sentences. If the sentence contains no error, select answer choice E.

1.   If Janine's sweater <u>was made</u> of better material, <u>it</u> <u>wouldn't have</u> frayed
                       (A)   (B)   (C)
     <u>so easily</u>.   <u>No error</u>
       (D)   (E)

2.   <u>Jenna always argues</u> with <u>her dad</u> because they never <u>agree to</u> <u>each other</u>
          (A)   (B)   (C)   (D)
     about anything.   <u>No error</u>
                      (E)

3.   Fishermen <u>must handle</u> bait <u>very carefully</u> <u>because</u> <u>you could get stuck</u>
                 (A)   (B)   (C)   (D)
     on the hook.   <u>No error</u>
                (E)

4.   The <u>most perfect ending</u> of the <u>well-publicized movie</u> we <u>attended was</u> a great
           (A)   (B)   (C)
     surprise <u>to us</u>.   <u>No error</u>
        (D)   (E)

5.   My <u>advise</u> to you is <u>to go down</u> to the police station and surrender <u>before this</u>
         (A)   (B)   (C)
     gets <u>any more</u> complicated.   <u>No error</u>
        (D)   (E)

Improving Sentences

The underlined portion of each sentence below contains some flaw. Select the answer choice that best corrects the flaw.

6.   Mental illness is diverse and complicated not only <u>to analyze but for assessing.</u>
     A.   to assess and for analysis.
     B.   to analyze, but also to assess.
     C.   for assessing, but also to analyze.
     D.   for analysis, but also to assess.
     E.   for assessment and analysis.

7. The basic difference among mature birds are their color pattern.
   A. The basic difference among mature birds is its color patterns.
   B. The basic differences among mature birds are their color patterns.
   C. The basic difference, among mature birds, are their color pattern.
   D. The basic differences among mature birds are their color pattern.
   E. The basic differences among mature birds is their color patterns.

8. Singers may dislike certain song lyrics, but that doesn't prove they are good or bad.
   A. Singers may dislike using certain lyrics in songs, but that doesn't prove they are good or bad.
   B. Even though singers disapprove of certain song lyrics they sing them, good or bad.
   C. A singer's dislike for certain song lyrics does not prove that they are good or bad.
   D. Good song lyrics or bad song lyrics, some singers dislike certain ones.
   E. Certain song lyrics are good and others are bad, but some singers who may dislike them sing them anyway.

9. The football team in their new uniforms, as well as the cheerleaders, and the exciting band music.
   A. The football team and the cheerleaders were in their new uniforms, and the band music was exciting.
   B. The cheerleaders, the football team, and the band were exciting in their new uniforms.
   C. The band music was exciting. As was the football team in their new uniforms, as well as the cheerleaders.
   D. In their new uniforms was the football team. The cheerleaders were, too, and the band music was exciting.
   E. The football team and cheerleaders were in their new uniforms with exciting band music.

10. The landlord denied the many charges that had been made against him, quickly and emphatically.
   A. Quickly and emphatically, the many charges that had been made against the landlord were denied.
   B. The many charges that had been made against the landlord quickly and emphatically, were denied.
   C. The many charges that had been made against him the landlord quickly and emphatically denied.
   D. Quickly and emphatically, the many charges that had been made against the landlord he denied.
   E. The landlord quickly and emphatically denied the many charges that had been made against him.

Lesson Fourteen

1. **catalyst** (kat´ ə list) *n.* a person, thing, or agent that causes or speeds up a reaction or change without itself being changed
   The atom bomb was a *catalyst* in ending World War II.
   syn: mechanism; vehicle; means

2. **jargon** (jär´ gən) *n.* vocabulary distinctive to a particular group of people
   Joe heard the attorneys exchanging legal *jargon*, but he understood little of it.
   syn: terminology; lingo

3. **judicious** (jōō dish´ əs) *adj.* showing sound judgment
   A *judicious* manager avoids favoritism and treats everyone the same way.
   syn: sensible; wise; careful   *ant: prejudicial; foolish*

4. **foible** (foi´ bəl) *n.* a minor weakness in character
   The chef's only *foible* was her forgetfulness.
   syn: fault; shortcoming

5. **benediction** (ben i dik´ shən) *n.* the act of blessing
   We bowed our heads for the *benediction* before singing the closing hymn.
                              ant: curse; malediction

6. **frivolous** (friv´ ə ləs) *adj.* trivial; silly
   They wasted time arguing over a *frivolous* matter.
   syn: inconsequential; vain   *ant: vital; important*

7. **alacrity** (ə lak´ ri tē) *n.* liveliness; willingness; eagerness
   He performed his chores with *alacrity* and finished them before noon.
   syn: enthusiasm; readiness; zeal   *ant: slowness; reluctance*

8. **deify** (dē´ ə fī) *v.* to make a god of; to look upon or worship as a god
   He *deified* her, but he soon discovered that she was as human as anyone else.
   syn: idolize; worship   *ant: abhor; detest*

9. **carnage** (kär´ nij) *n.* bloody and extensive slaughter
   United Nations forces were deployed to end the *carnage* in the war-torn nation.
   syn: bloodshed; slaughter

10. **impel** (im pel´) *v.* to push into motion
    The man's thirst *impelled* him to continue walking along the desert highway.
    syn: urge; force; propel; drive   *ant: restrain*

11. **epitaph** (ep´ i tâf)   *n.*   an inscription on a tombstone; a brief comment about a deceased person
The tombstone had the simple *epitaph*, "Rest In Peace."

12. **harp** (härp)   *v.*   to persist in talking continuously (on or about something)
My parents *harp* on the importance of completing homework.
syn: ramble; complain

13. **lateral** (lat´ ər əl)   *adj.*   of or relating to the side
Bill made a *lateral* career move by taking a new job with no change in salary.
syn: sideways

14. **pallid** (pal´ id)   *adj.*   pale; faint in color
The patient's *pallid* face and labored breathing concerned the doctor.
syn: colorless   *ant: hearty; robust*

15. **impetuous** (im pech´ ōō əs)   *adj.*   acting suddenly without thought
Impetuous behavior can be hazardous to your health.
syn: impulsive; rash   *ant: planned; careful*

Exercise I

Words in Context

From the list below, supply the words needed to complete the paragraph. Some words will not be used.

frivolous	alacrity	deify	catalyst
foible	harp	impetuous	

1. Steve never realized it, but his single _____ was his _____ in complaining about _____ things that do not even bother most people; for example, if a waiter brought Steve the wrong beverage, Steve _____ about the mistake for days. Fortunately, he was not so _____ as to cause embarrassing scenes in public.

From the list below, supply the words needed to complete the paragraph. Some words will not be used.

deify	jargon	epitaph	harp
carnage	pallid	impel	

2. Bonnie was an apprentice, so she didn't understand all the archaeological _____ spoken around the dig site; however, she did understand the theories on what the farmer had discovered. Statues found near an altar implied that the ancient tribe used to _____ certain animals and worship them in ceremonies. A large amount of fractured skeletal remains at the dig site suggested that the tribe was also particularly violent; Bonnie's face grew _____ when she paused to think about the _____ that had taken place at the ancient site. The remains of hundreds of people lay in the sacrificial pit without a single marker or _____ to mark their resting place.

From the list below, supply the words needed to complete the paragraph. Some words will not be used.

judicious	foible	catalyst	benediction
lateral	impel	alacrity	

3. The family business had a history of making _____ moves that netted no profit until Lynn took over and found ways to increase revenue; however, even though she was a[n] _____ for the company's success, Lynn hated her job. She _____ her father to seek a good replacement for her, but he never did. At dinner one evening, shortly after the _____, Lynn announced that she had been offered a job with a larger company at twice her current salary. To Lynn's surprise, her father congratulated her and complimented her for making a[n] _____ decision.

Exercise II

Sentence Completion

Complete the sentence in a way that shows you understand the meaning of the italicized vocabulary word.

1. Since you made an *impetuous* remark to the restaurant manager, I don't want to…

2. Too much *lateral* stress on the telephone pole caused it to…

3. They could not read the *epitaph* because…

4. Few could imagine the *carnage* that had taken place at…

5. For summer help at the factory, the boss wanted teenagers with the *alacrity* to…

6. After the reverend gave the *benediction*, everyone at the banquet…

7. The broker made a series of *judicious* investments that…

8. The new quarterback was the *catalyst* for the team's…

9. Pat's face turned *pallid* when…

10. Ken put on headphones because he could no longer stand to hear Mike *harp* about…

11. The onset of war *impelled* many people to…

12. The ancient civilization *deified* their priests; regular citizens were not even allowed to…

13. The used car was as ugly in color as it was in shape, but these were only *frivolous* concerns to Clint because he…

14. Though the billionaire gives millions to charity each year, many people refuse to look beyond his odd *foible* of…

15. You should become familiar with nautical *jargon* if you plan to…

Exercise III

Roots, Prefixes, and Suffixes

Study the entries and answer the questions that follow.

The roots *stru* and *struct* mean "to build."
The roots *tempor* and *temper* mean "time."
The root *therm* means "heat."

1. Using *literal* translations as guidance, define the following words without using a dictionary:

    A. thermostat   D. destruct
    B. instrument   E. structure
    C. hypothermia   F. contemporary

2. A *thermometer* measures _____. If you want your coffee to retain its heat, then you might put it in a[n] _____. A branch of science that deals with the study of heat is called _____-dynamics.

3. A[n] _____ worker is hired for a limited time only. In science fiction, a disruption in time might be described as a[n] _____ disturbance.

4. List as many words as you can think of that contain the roots *tempor, temper, stru,* or *struct.*

Exercise IV

Inference

Complete the sentence by inferring information about the italicized word from its context.

1. Penny didn't demonstrate the *alacrity* to play soccer, so the coach…

2. Hearing an exciting account about discovering lost treasure might *impel* an inspired listener to…

3. If the boss tells the workmen to ignore any *frivolous* concerns and simply get the job done, then the boss doesn't want the workers to worry about…

Exercise V

Critical Reading

Below is a reading passage followed by several multiple-choice questions. Carefully read the passage and choose the best answer for each of the questions.

The U.S. Fish and Wildlife Service operates the Fisheries Program and has been in existence for over 100 years. Some of the issues that inspired the program's creation are still being addressed today.

1   Americans love fish. We catch them for food, for recreation, and for income. We photograph them, we display them on walls, and we watch them in aquariums. We pursue brook trout in pristine wilderness and catfish in crowded urban waters; however, habitat degradation, pollution, dams, competition from invasive species, and over-harvesting threaten America's vital aquatic resource.

2   At one time, America's pristine waters supported plentiful and robust fisheries. Our nation's natural treasures appeared to be unlimited until the Industrial Revolution and population surge required vast quantities of natural resources, notably water, timber, minerals, and wildlife. During this period, water quality and fish resources endured a rapid decline.

3   By the mid-1800s, fishermen identified that there was a decrease in fish populations. In 1871, Spencer Fullerton Baird, Assistant Secretary of the Smithsonian Institution, wrote to Congress urging Federal protection for the nation's fisheries. Baird warned that America would lose fish as a way of life and lifestyle, and that such a calamity would leave a series of evils in its wake.

4   **Impelled** by threatened fish populations, Congress created the Commission on Fish and Fisheries, which is now called the U.S. Fish and Wildlife Service (FWS). It was the first federal agency dedicated to the conservation of natural resources. The first objective of the commission was to determine whether fisheries had indeed declined and to plot a **judicious** course of action.

5   The present Fish and Wildlife Service still upholds the mission to restore our fisheries by surveying populations and habitats, raising native fish and other species, and restoring habitats to meet the goals of fisheries' management plans. To fulfill these far-reaching objectives, the Fish and Wildlife Service maintains a network of field stations across the country, including seventy hatcheries and one genetics laboratory.

6   One of the most important objectives of the Fish and Wildlife Service is to moderate declining native fish populations by restoring and protecting habitats and reintroducing fish where appropriate. In addition to stocking, the FWS also works to recover species listed under the Endangered Species Act by monitoring and evaluating fish populations. Using databases, the FWS conducts long-term monitoring to track the health and relative abundance of fish resources; the recorded data can then be used to create the appropriate protective measures to sustain specific ecosystems.

7   In the area of habitat conservation and management, the Fish and Wildlife Service determines habitat needs for fish populations and functions as a **catalyst** for accomplishing the necessary improvements. Because dams and other man-made barriers threaten many fish populations, the program works with other federal, state, and local agencies to advocate high water quality and availability of passage in streams and rivers.

8   The Fish and Wildlife Service also provides leadership in the development and application of state-of-the-art science and technology for conservation of fish and other aquatic species. Fish health centers inspect hatchery fish for pathogens, diagnose diseases, and then recommend remedial treatments to improve fish health management. Some wild fish, such as the endangered Pacific salmon, require close monitoring of their health to ensure their recovery. This monitoring also prevents species from becoming threatened or endangered.

9   The Fish and Wildlife Service is a government organization, but that does not mean that it interacts exclusively with other government agencies. It is currently working in partnership with Native American Tribal Nations whose **lateral** goals of restoring fish and wildlife improve the land's capacity for fishing and hunting. Cooperation between the Fish and Wildlife Service and the White Mountain Apache Tribe, for example, has already been successful in recovering the once-endangered Apache trout. The trout is now on the threatened list instead of the endangered list, and the improvement indicates that the trout and its habitat are almost fully restored.

10   Our American heritage includes a rich history of recreational fishing, and the Fish and Wildlife Service helps ensure its future. In the Southeast alone, the FWS releases more than six million fish in an attempt to enhance sport-fishing opportunities and to mitigate the negative impact of federal dams.

11   Despite a century of progress, however, America's fish are still in danger. The Fish and Wildlife Service is more important than ever as aquatic habitats decline due to erosion, sedimentation, altered stream flows, dams, obstructions, pollution, and invasive species. Through diligent application of sound science, effective management practices, and dedicated partnerships, the Fish and Wildlife Service will continue to conserve species and their habitats and, thus, ensure the future of America's fishing tradition.

1A. Which of the following best describes the main idea of the passage?
    A.   Fishing is an American national pastime, thanks to wildlife management.
    B.   Industrialization has reduced the fish population in the United States.
    C.   The Fish and Wildlife Service is dedicated to conserving fish and their habitats.
    D.   The nation's water quality has declined.
    E.   The Fish and Wildlife Service creates recreational fishing opportunities.

1B. Choose the best description of the tone of the passage.
    A.   defensive about the purpose of the FWS
    B.   dismissive about FWS history
    C.   deeply concerned about pollution
    D.   positive about the role of the FWS
    E.   indifferent toward fish and fisheries

2A. As used in paragraph 3, *fisheries* most nearly means
    A.   places in which fish are raised by people.
    B.   places in which fish are stored.
    C.   lakes and ponds.
    D   places in which fish are caught.
    E.   coastal fishing regions.

2B. Which line from the passage provides the best evidence for your answer to question 2A?
    A.   "Impelled by threatened fish populations"
    B.   "fish as a way of life and lifestyle"
    C.   "conservation of natural resources"
    D.   "whether fisheries had indeed declined"
    E.   "by...raising native fish and other species"

3A. Which of the following events led to a decline in fish population?
  A.   the Industrial Revolution
  B.   the Civil War
  C.   illegal fishing practices
  D.   acidic water conditions due to mine drainage
  E.   the inaction of Spencer Fullerton Baird

3B. Based on your answer to 3A and the text, what directly caused the decline?
  A.   loss of natural predators
  B.   housing developments
  C.   bad water
  D.   imbalance of native species
  E.   overfishing

4A. As it is used in paragraph 6, the word *stocking* most nearly means
  A.   harvesting.
  B.   eliminating.
  C.   helping.
  D.   transplanting.
  E.   retaining.

4B. Choose the phrase from the text that provides the best evidence for your answer to question 4A.
  A.   "restoring and protecting habitats"
  B.   "FWS also works to recover species"
  C.   "track the health and relative abundance of fish resources"
  D.   "monitoring and evaluating fish populations"
  E.   "reintroducing fish where appropriate"

5.   The author notes that the Fish and Wildlife Service helps the White Mountain Apache Tribe, which shows
  A.   the tribe's food supply was vanishing.
  B.   the Apache trout is the most popular sport fish in the United States.
  C.   the agency also works with groups outside the government.
  D.   concern for the Native American Tribal Nations.
  E.   the tribe will convince Congress to allocate more funds to the Fish and Wildlife Service.

6A. According to the passage, which answer places the terms in the order of best to worst?
  A.   extinct, threatened, endangered
  B.   endangered, extinct, threatened
  C.   threatened, extinct, endangered
  D.   threatened, endangered, extinct
  E.   endangered, threatened, extinct

6B. Which fish is used as the example that provides evidence for your answer to question 6A?
   A. channel catfish
   B. Apache trout
   C. brook trout
   D. Pacific salmon
   E. native yellow perch

7. Which of the following is *not* a present danger to fish habitats, based on information in the passage?
   A. sport fishing
   B. sediment in the water
   C. the rerouting of waterways
   D. industrial waste
   E. dam building

8A. Which of the following best describes the tone of the passage?
   A. lively and entertaining
   B. thoughtful and optimistic
   C. droll and witty
   D. scholarly and substantial
   E. dry and unemotional

8B. This passage is written in the perspective of someone who
   A. is probably foreign.
   B. works for the Fish and Wildlife Service.
   C. is a museum curator.
   D. is American, but not necessarily a member of the FWS.
   E. believes in governmental non-intervention.

9A. Which of the following would be an appropriate title for this passage?
   A. Native and Aquatic Nuisance Species
   B. Leadership in Aquatic Natural Science
   C. Preserving America's Fisheries
   D. Aquatic Habitat Conservation and Management
   E. U.S. Fishery Resources

9B. Which would be the most accurate subtitle for the passage, in order to extend the title?
   A. The Purpose of the Fish and Wildlife Service
   B. 100 Years of Freshwater Sportfishing
   C. America's Favorite Tradition
   D. Eliminating Dams and Stopping Pollution
   E. A Time of Uncertainty for Fish

10A. This passage would most likely be found in a/an
  A.   encyclopedia.
  B.   popular fishing newsletter.
  C.   academic journal.
  D.   science textbook.
  E.   newspaper.

10B. Which choice best explains your answer to question 10A?
  A.   The specific dates and procedures described connote a scholarly purpose.
  B.   A focus on local history suggests the text's small intended audience.
  C.   Judgmental tones toward polluters make the text most suited for an opinion column.
  D.   The informal use of "we" and "our" gives the reader a personal connection to the text.
  E.   The use of slang words and figurative language render the text most suited for entertainment.

Lesson Fifteen

1. **adjunct** (a´jûngkt) *adj.* connected or attached to in a dependent,
   subordinate, or auxiliary manner, but not an inherent part of
   Dr. Jones, who teaches only one class, is an *adjunct* faculty member at the university,
   not a full professor.

2. **macabre** (mə käb´) *adj.* horrible; grim
   The *macabre* paintings featured torture scenes from the Spanish Inquisition.
   syn: ghastly; sinister   *ant: beautiful; lovely*

3. **farcical** (fär´ si kəl) *adj.* absurd; ridiculously clumsy
   The botched bank robbery became *farcical* when the getaway car broke down.
   syn: ludicrous; funny   *ant: somber; serious*

4. **debonair** (deb ə nâr´) *adj.* carefree and self-confident in manner; elegant
   and gracious
   I expected to see an awkward young man, but instead I saw a *debonair* gentleman.
   syn: charming; refined; suave   *ant: gauche; awkward*

5. **penchant** (pen´ chənt) *n.* a strong liking
   She had a *penchant* for tiny dogs because she had one when she was a child.
   syn: fondness; inclination; taste   *ant: dislike; abhorrence*

6. **deplete** (di plēt´) *v.* to use up gradually
   If we *deplete* our limited food supply, we will have to hunt for food.
   syn: empty; exhaust   *ant: replenish*

7. **chicanery** (shi kā´ nə rē) *n.* the use of tricks or clever talk to deceive or evade
   The con artist used old-fashioned *chicanery* to steal credit card information.
   syn: trickery; subterfuge   *ant: honesty*

8. **feisty** (fī´ stē) *adj.* aggressive; lively; energetic
   The tiger cub was small but *feisty*, so we approached him with caution.
   syn: spirited; frisky   *ant: lethargic*

9. **mitigate** (mit´ i gāt) *v.* to make less severe; to become milder
   Gary put plywood over the windows to *mitigate* any damage that the hurricane might
   do to his house.
   syn: diminish; alleviate   *ant: aggravate; exacerbate*

10. **gull**   (gul)   *v.*   to cheat; to fool or hoax
The man in the carnival booth *gulled* me out of twenty dollars.
syn: dupe; scam; trick

11. **nadir**   (nā´ dər)   *n.*   the lowest point
Getting fired was the *nadir* of Bob's terrible week.
syn: bottom   *ant: peak; zenith*

12. **equivocal**   (i kwiv´ ə kəl)   *adj.*   ambiguous; intentionally vague
His answer was *equivocal*, despite my plea for a simple "Yes" or "No."
syn: uncertain; cryptic   *ant: certain; definite*

13. **genealogy**   (jē nē al´ ə jē)   *n.*   family history
The family tree depicted his *genealogy*.
syn: lineage; heredity

14. **impervious**   (im pûr´ vē əs)   *adj.*   incapable of being affected
The wounded soldier, apparently *impervious* to pain, continued to fight.
syn: resistant; invulnerable   *ant: vulnerable*

15. **filial**   (fil´ ē əl)   *adj.*   of, relating to, or befitting a son or daughter
They were not related, but Sam exhibited an almost *filial* respect for his mentor.

Exercise I

Words in Context

From the list below, supply the words needed to complete the paragraph. Some words will not be used.

deplete	feisty	gull	equivocal
mitigate	chicanery	filial	

1. In an effort to _____ costs, the Lockwoods asked their neighbor, Bob, about installing a new roof on their house. Bob, a carpenter, advised them not to let some phony contractor _____ them into paying for something they didn't need. The existing roof needed only a simple repair, Bob said, and there was no need for the Lockwoods to _____ their savings for unnecessary construction. He knew that some so-called discount contractors frequently used _____ and _____ estimates to cheat clients.

From the list below, supply the words needed to complete the paragraph. Some words will not be used.

genealogy	debonair	nadir	chicanery
farcical	penchant	feisty	

2. Oscar Wilde's _____ for satire shows in his play, *The Importance of Being Earnest*. This energetic play is a _____ comedy in which _____ characters, usually depicted as refined, _____ members of the Victorian upper class, turn out to be argumentative fools. At the end of the play, the two central characters, who are friends, discover that they share the same _____ and that they are actually brothers.

From the list below, supply the words needed to complete the paragraph. Some words will not be used.

mitigate	macabre	filial	farcical
impervious	adjunct	nadir	

3. Frank thought that a camping trip might be a good way to improve his _____ relationship with his son and daughter, whom he rarely saw due to his long work hours. He planned a hike from the summit to the _____ of a canyon and then picked out a nice spot on the map where they could pitch tents for the night and scare each other with _____ stories around the campfire. Frank thought that the kids would jump at the idea; unfortunately, they did not.

    "Dad," moaned Tim, "you know that I'm busy this weekend." Frank looked as if he were listening to his son, but he was actually _____ to the protest.

    "Oh, come on," said Frank, automatically. "We'll have a great time. I used to be a[n] _____ counselor for a camp—"

    "A *basketball* camp," interrupted Lisa. "And everyone knows that basketball camps are not exactly where people go to learn wilderness survival skills."

Exercise II

Sentence Completion

Complete the sentence in a way that shows you understand the meaning of the italicized vocabulary word.

1. One *macabre* room at the haunted house contained...

2. The *debonair* hero of the novel waltzed right into the villain's hideout and...

3. If we *deplete* Earth's natural resources too soon, the world will...

4. Bill broke his arm when the *feisty* horse...

5. Police put out a warning for a man who *gulls* people by claiming to be...

6. Tony's *equivocal* answer to our question caused...

7. After three weeks of being the new kid at school, Dawn became *impervious* to...

8. Janice is a full-time writer, but in the evenings, she is an *adjunct* instructor at...

9. Barbara was tired of watching *farcical* movies, so she decided...

10. Mary-Ellen had a *penchant* for the outdoors, so for her vacation, she...

11. The used-car salesman sometimes used *chicanery* to...

12. One way to *mitigate* the swelling of a sprained ankle is to...

13. During the *nadir* of her career, Tina...

14. The chart in the history book shows the *genealogy* of...

15. On the frontier, if parents had to leave their homestead, it was a *filial* duty for the children to...

| **Exercise III** |

Roots, Prefixes, and Suffixes

Study the entries and answer the questions that follow.

The suffix –*ion* means "the act of."
The root *cret* means "to separate," "to decide," or "to distinguish."
The root *spir* means "to breathe."

1. Using *literal* translations as guidance, define the following words without using a dictionary:

    A. secretary   D. spirit
    B. excrete   E. conspire
    C. secretion   F. inspiration

2. The government might mark certain classified information as being _____, to distinguish it from ordinary information. People who have the special information must use _____ in deciding who receives it because a leak could compromise national security.

3. Someone who needs help breathing might use a[n] _____. A story that breathes life into you might be said to _____ you.

4. List as many words as you can think of that contain the suffix –*ion*.

| **Exercise IV** |

Inference

Complete the sentence by inferring information about the italicized word from its context.

1. If you have a *penchant* for working with children because they like to learn, then you might…

2. Two extra lodgers during the winter in the mountains might cause you to *deplete* your food supply quickly, so before winter, you should…

3. If the prisoner appears to be *impervious* to rehabilitation, the parole board will probably…

Exercise V

Writing

Here is a writing prompt similar to the one you will find on the writing portion of an assessment test.

Plan and write an essay based on the following statement:

> That all men are equal is a proposition to which, at ordinary times, no sane individual has ever given his assent.
>
> –Aldous Huxley, *Proper Studies*

Assignment: Conflicting perspectives of human equality have been a source of unrest for thousands of years, but Aldous Huxley claims that no normal person would ever admit that all people are equal. Does Huxley's quote apply to mankind as a whole or individually? In an essay, indicate whether you agree or disagree with Huxley, explain his quote, and then explain the level of human existence to which it is supposed to apply.

Thesis: Write a *one-sentence* response to the assignment. Make certain this single sentence offers a clear statement of your position.

Example: Aldous Huxley's suggestion that not all people are equal is correct because there are certain things that some people can do that others can't, no matter how hard they might try.

———————————————————————————————

———————————————————————————————

Organizational Plan: List at least three subtopics you will use to support your main idea. This list is your outline.

1. ————————————————————————————

2. ————————————————————————————

3. ————————————————————————————

Draft: Following your outline, write a good first draft of your essay. Remember to support all your points with examples, facts, references to reading, etc.

Review and Revise: Exchange essays with a classmate. Using the scoring guide for Sentence Formation and Variety on page 254, score your partner's essay (while he or she scores yours). Focus on sentence structure and the use of language conventions. If necessary, rewrite your essay to improve the sentence structure and/or your use of language.

Exercise VI

Improving Paragraphs

Read the following passage and then answer the multiple-choice questions that follow. The questions will require you to make decisions regarding the revision of the reading selection.

1   (1) The thunderhead, with its spires reaching miles into the evening sky, cast a shadowy curtain on the shoreline as the sun settled below the opposite horizon. (2) Helios retreated from Poseidon, and for good reason: the approaching fiend was quite possibly the largest tempest to strike the grainy shore in months.

2   (3) Torrential rain followed the hail. (4) The sand on and near the beach became so saturated with water that streams formed among the weeds and occasionally washed creatures out onto the open beach. (5) Few were able to cling to the sand after one pass of the surging seawater.

3   (6) The number of scuttling beach residents diminished with the last few rays of light. (7) Most of them were scavengers seeking food scraps from decaying horseshoe crabs, only vaguely aware that something bad approached their community. (8) They made clicking noises as they scurried across the wet sand, over the dunes, and into the tall grass, where it burrowed to hide from the pending onslaught. (9) Storms like this were known to cause flash floods. (10) Those near the water simply disappeared into the rising surf; not one reappeared in the frothing brine that each wave carried further inland. (11) A flock of noisy seagulls concluded their hour-long battle over a wet fast-food bag and allowed the gales to carry them inland, where they huddled beneath the joists of condemned homes and the rafters of corrugated warehouses. (12) They sat silent and inert, as though their instinct to overcome hunger for safety had turned them into an entirely different species. (13) Unlike the rest of the beach life, the birds were **impervious** of the storm.

4   (14) All but the simplest order of creatures experienced panic when the first wave of hailstones tore through vegetation and threw sand from miniature impact craters. (15) The icy projectiles, some the size of apples, stung the backs of exposed wildlife huddled in the grass. (16) Smaller crustaceans did not fare as well; hail smashed exoskeletons and leg joints. (17) They would become food for their neighbors after the storm.

5   (18) The worst of the storm lasted only minutes, but it eliminated all but a fraction of the beach colony. (19) Most had been swept into the dark abyss beneath the starless void, and, in their relatively short lives, they would never be able to battle the riptide to return to the sands on which they spent their lives before the storm. (20) Those left in the open, disoriented from tumbling in the surf, would become a **macabre** feast for the cackling gang of seagulls when it returned to continue its feeding frenzy.

1.   What change would improve the chronological order of the paragraphs?
    A.   Exchange paragraphs 1 and 2.
    B.   Exchange paragraphs 2 and 3.
    C.   Move paragraph 2 after paragraph 4.
    D.   Move paragraph 1 after paragraph 4.
    E.   Delete paragraph 2.

2.   Which of the following corrects the grammatical error in sentence 8?
    A.   Replace *where it burrowed* with *where they burrowed*.
    B.   Replace *they* with *horseshoe crabs*.
    C.   Replace the comma after *grass* with a semicolon.
    D.   Capitalize *dunes*.
    E.   Delete *across*.

3. If the passage had to be shortened, which sentence could be removed without harming the intent of the passage?
    A. sentence 6
    B. sentence 7
    C. sentence 8
    D. sentence 9
    E. sentence 10

4. Which of the following best improves the underlined portion of sentence 13?

    Unlike the rest of the beach life, <u>the birds were impervious of the storm</u>.

    A. the impervious birds were saved from the storm.
    B. the birds were impervious to the storm.
    C. the impervious birds were safe.
    D. the birds were impervious during the storm.
    E. the birds were more impervious.

5. Which change would best make paragraph 3 easier to read?
    A. Delete sentence 6.
    B. Exchange paragraph 3 with paragraph 5.
    C. Include more descriptions of seagulls.
    D. Begin a new paragraph after sentence 10.
    E. Begin a new paragraph after sentence 11.

Review Lessons 13-15

Exercise I

Inferences

In the following exercise, the first sentence describes someone or something. Infer information from the first sentence, and then choose the word from the Word Bank that best completes the second sentence.

catalyst	jargon	equivocal	denigrate
effusive	mitigate	impetuous	anachronism

1. The children always seem to fight over who gets to play with the castle playset, so Mom put it away in the attic.

    From this sentence, we can infer that the castle playset is a[n] _____ that causes conflict among the children.

2. The adventure novel was good, but it was difficult to overlook its inclusion of inventions that did not exist until centuries after the book's setting.

    From this sentence, we can infer that the novel contains _____ that diminish its quality.

3. Knowing that the neighborhood would soon be under floodwaters, residents quickly moved their belongings to the upper levels of their homes.

    From this sentence, we can infer that the residents attempted to _____ the damage that the flood would cause.

4. When asked where she stood on the controversial issue, the senator spoke for ten minutes without even answering the question.

    From this sentence, we can infer that the senator provided a[n] _____ reply to the question.

5. Martin spent his whole savings as a down payment on an expensive car, ignoring the fact that he would not be able to afford the monthly payments.

    From this sentence, we can infer that Martin probably made a[n] _____ purchase.

Exercise II

Related Words

Some of the vocabulary words from Lessons 13 through 15 have related meanings. Complete the following sentences by choosing the word that best fits the context, based on information you infer from the use of the italicized word. Some word pairs will be antonyms, some will be synonyms, and some will simply be words often used in the same context.

1. Maria began planting trees with *alacrity* early in the summer morning, but by 11:00 am, the 90-degree heat _____ her energy so much that she could barely swing the shovel.
   A. gaped
   B. gulled
   C. depleted
   D. harped
   E. embroiled

2. Aunt Pat *denigrated* her forty-year-old son every day for living in her basement and playing video games all day instead of looking for a job; however, she secretly hoped that her nagging would _____ the man to start living his own life.
   A. envisage
   B. impel
   C. harp
   D. filch
   E. deify

3. The Explosive Ordnance Disposal team wore protective suits designed to be _____ to the *lethal* chemical nerve agent leaking from the old artillery shell.
   A. filial
   B. effusive
   C. judicious
   D. indisposed
   E. impervious

4. As soon as the *defunct* video game console reached a _____ in sales, it was removed from stores.
   A. nadir
   B. decadence
   C. nemesis
   D. holocaust
   E. jargon

5. Seeing an airplane flying in the background of the cowboy movie was such a[n]
   _____ that it turned a serious film into a *farcical* one.
   A. epitaph
   B. chicanery
   C. anachronism
   D. benediction
   E. catalyst

6. The cult leader surrounded himself with _____ who carried out the dirty work
   for the man they *deified*.
   A. nemeses
   B. lackeys
   C. jargon
   D. nadirs
   E. laggards

7. When asked for an explanation of the catastrophic failure of the rocket, the nervous
   scientist provided a[n] _____ answer that would have confused his bosses even
   if they had understood the *jargon* in which the physicist spoke.
   A. debonair
   B. frivolous
   C. equivocal
   D. choleric
   E. humane

8. Terry stood out among the *debonair* crowd at the exclusive charity ball, mostly
   because he wore a baby blue tuxedo, ate straight from the snack tray, and made
   _____ remarks about the guest speakers.
   A. impervious
   B. fallow
   C. defunct
   D. impertinent
   E. adjunct

9. After experiencing the *carnage* of a battle fought at close range with axes and swords, the
   young soldier swore to live a[n] _____ life of charity and compassion.
   A. effusive
   B. humane
   C. lateral
   D. impertinent
   E. futile

10. Over the years, the family learned to avoid discussion of politics at holiday dinners
    because the subject was a[n] _____ for conflict and guaranteed to *embroil*
    everyone at the table in a screaming match.
    A. holocaust
    B. status quo
    C. nemesis
    D. anachronism
    E. catalyst

Exercise III

Deeper Meanings

Choose a word to replace the italicized word in each sentence. All of the possible choices for each sentence have similar definitions, but the correct answer will have a connotation that best suits the context. For example, the words "delete," "destroy," and "obliterate" all mean "to remove or wipe out," but no one would ever say, "I destroyed the name from the document." The correct choice will be the word that has the best specific meaning and does not render the sentence awkward in tone or content. When choices seem close, look for a clue in the context that makes one choice better than the other.

Note that the correct answer is not always the primary vocabulary word from the lesson.

lackeys	nervous	dead	impelled
uncontrollable	defunct	creative	slaves
moved	companions	judicious	cruel
insecure			

1. Kim always feels very *feisty* before her track meets; she has to take deep breaths to keep her hands from shaking until the starting pistol goes off.

    Better word: _____

2. The company was once the largest manufacturer of steam boilers in the world, but it failed to adapt to new technology and is now *invalid*.

    Better word: _____

3. The schoolyard bully's *helpers* are cowards who pick on other kids, but then hide behind the bully if anyone fights back.

    Better word: _____

4. The *smart* king offered to split the baby in two to see which of the two women would rather give up custody than see her child harmed, and the woman who did so was the child's true mother.

    Better word: _____

5. A sudden, blinding flash of lightning just across the fairway *urged* the golfers to drop their irons and run for the clubhouse.

    Better word: _____

Exercise IV

Crossword Puzzle

Use the clues to complete the crossword puzzle. The answers consist of vocabulary words from Lessons 13 through 15.

Across

4. worship
6. creepy
8. out of time
13. use the last drop
14. swiftness
15. shop talk
17. regret
18. to the side

Down

1. suave
2. go on and on and on
3. family tree
5. far from serious
7. deadly
9. imagine
10. speak ill of
11. way out of style
12. pale as a ghost
16. rock bottom

Exercise V

Subject Prompts

Here is a writing prompt similar to the one you will find on the writing portion of an assessment test. Follow the instructions below and write a brief, efficient essay.

> With the rise in the frequency of flash mobs, some cities have imposed early curfews upon minors. Curfews are not uncommon during times of catastrophe or martial law, but are they fair in normal times? Do curfews comply with the tenets of a free society, or do they tread close to tyranny? Do minors have legitimate reasons to be on the streets at night, or should they even need a reason?
>
> Take a position on the use of youth curfews and explain it in a letter to the editor of a city newspaper. Support your argument with three examples or subtopics detailing why curfews are appropriate or inappropriate means of maintaining order.

Thesis: Write a *one-sentence* response to the assignment. Make certain this single sentence offers a clear statement of your position.

Example: A curfew is one of the ultimate abuses of the rights of teenagers.

_____

_____

Organizational Plan: List at least three subtopics you will use to support your main idea. This list is your outline.

1. _____

2. _____

3. _____

Draft: Following your outline, write a good first draft of your essay. Remember to support all your points with examples, facts, references to reading, etc.

Review and Revise: Exchange essays with a classmate. Using the Holistic scoring guide on page 256, score your partner's essay (while he or she scores yours). If necessary, rewrite your essay to correct the problems noted by your partner.

Lesson Sixteen

1. **daub** (dôb) *v.* to paint coarsely or unskillfully
Painting requires patience and consistency; you cannot simply *daub* the canvas with a paint-laden brush.
syn: smear

2. **admonish** (ad mon´ ish) *v.* to warn; to caution in counsel
The lifeguard *admonished* the children for swimming beyond the buoys.
syn: advise; notify; warn   *ant: compliment; approve*

3. **obeisance** (ō bā´ səns) *n.* a bow or similar gesture expressing deep respect
The villager rendered *obeisance* as the king's entourage passed.

4. **cache** (kash) *n.* a concealed store of goods or valuables
While the campers were canoeing on the lake, bears raided their *cache* of food.
syn: hoard; reserve

5. **affliction** (ə flik´ shən) *n.* anything causing great suffering
Heatstroke can be a lethal *affliction* if not treated.
syn: difficulty; pain; burden   *ant: relief; aid*

6. **mendicant** (men´ di kənt) *n.* a beggar
The tourists tried to avoid the *mendicants* sitting in front of the gift shop.

7. **aphorism** (af´ ə rizm) *n.* a concise statement of a truth or principle
My father lives by the *aphorism* "Waste not, want not."
syn: adage; maxim; saying

8. **oscillate** (os´ ə lāt) *v.* to swing or move back and forth like a pendulum
Your opinion of the movie will probably *oscillate* from good to bad until you have more time to think about it.
syn: vacillate; fluctuate; alternate   *ant: steady*

9. **delete** (di lēt´, dē) *v.* to take out; to remove
You can *delete* the third sentence because it is unnecessary.
syn: erase; cancel   *ant: include; add*

10. **oust** (oust) *v.* to drive out; to expel; to deprive
The bailiff *ousted* the noisy courtroom spectators.
syn: eject

11. **impermeable**   (im pûr′ mē ə bəl)   *adj.*   not permitting passage
       (especially of fluids)
    The parka has an *impermeable* layer that keeps you dry.
    syn: impenetrable; impervious   *ant: permeable*

12. **paean**   (pē′ än)   *n.*   a fervent expression, or song, of joy or praise
    The book is simply a *paean* to the candidate; it lists his achievements, but not
    his failures.
    syn: acclaim; tribute

13. **smug**   (smug)   *adj.*   excessively self-satisfied
    The *smug* captain swore nothing on Earth could sink his ship.
    syn: complacent; conceited   *ant: modest; uncertain*

14. **lax**   (laks)   *adj.*   careless or negligent
    Don't become too *lax* in your studies, or you'll fail.
    syn: slack; neglectful   *ant: careful; meticulous*

15. **palpable**   (pal′ pə bəl)   *adj.*   obvious; capable of being touched or felt
    The fear in the room was so *palpable* that Tim thought he could almost taste it.
    syn: evident; conspicuous

Exercise I

Words in Context

From the list below, supply the words needed to complete the paragraph. Some words will not be used.

| admonish | affliction | lax | smug |
| delete | obeisance | oust | |

1. Everyone knew that Kiplar was an outsider when he failed to give _____ to the passing queen. One of the royal escorts immediately spotted Kiplar and walked over to _____ him for his failure to show respect.

   "What is this _____ of yours that prevents you from taking a knee upon sight of our queen? Shall we _____ you from your sleepy village and see how you fare in a dungeon?" The guard's threat did not faze the _____ man. Kiplar, still standing, simply smiled.

From the list below, supply the words needed to complete the paragraph. Some words will not be used.

| paean | aphorism | affliction | impermeable |
| palpable | lax | daub | |

2. Justin began to have second thoughts about his summer job when the temperature rose to ninety degrees. For the third day in a row, he stood on a flimsy ladder and _____ maroon paint onto the side of Mrs. Bailey's house. He wore no gloves today; yesterday, he discovered that the cheap cotton painter's gloves were not _____ when he removed them and found his hands stained maroon. To make matters worse, Mrs. Bailey frequently came outside to ensure that Justin hadn't become _____ on the job. The old _____, "time flies when you're having fun," couldn't have been more applicable to Justin, because each ten-hour day of painting felt like an eternity. If hard work builds character, thought Justin, then he should have a[n] _____ amount of character after this job.

From the list below, supply the words needed to complete the paragraph. Some words will not be used.

| paean | delete | oust | mendicant |
| cache | oscillate | palpable | |

3. In the late afternoon, Marvin opened the bottom drawer of his desk to reveal a[n] _____ of snack cakes and little bags of potato chips. He helped himself to a cream-filled cupcake as he perused his e-mail messages and _____ any old ones that were just taking up space on the computer's hard drive. A heavy fan _____ in the corner of the office, causing self-adhesive notes and thumb-tacked comic strips to flap around in the breeze every few seconds. Next to the fan was a tied trash bag full of empty aluminum soda cans for Joe, a[n] _____ who lived in the alley behind the magazine publisher. Joe, who chose the streets over shelters, inspired many people at the office, and he had no idea that Marvin's next article was going to be a[n] _____ to the homeless who have learned to sustain themselves despite their austere living conditions.

Exercise II

Sentence Completion

Complete the sentence in a way that shows you understand the meaning of the italicized vocabulary word.

1. The sprinkler head *oscillates* so that the entire lawn...

2. The book began with the old *aphorism*, "...

3. The magazine editor told the writer to *delete*...

4. A *mendicant* outside the grocery store asked me...

5. Bouncers at the club *ousted* Herbert because he...

6. The Arctic explorers could not find their *cache* of supplies because...

7. If you wear boots that are *impermeable*, you won't have to worry about...

8. The *affliction* became widespread when villagers drank water from...

9. The National Anthem is a *paean* to...

10. The young student bowed his head in *obeisance* to...

11. Renee has been wearing a *smug* expression ever since...

12. I'll *admonish* you this time, but the next time you do it, I'm going to...

13. The *lax* worker at the power plant failed to notice that...

14. Some people like the way in which the artist randomly *daubs* bright colors onto the large canvas, but others think...

15. Your promises are great, but if you don't show some *palpable* progress on the project, the teacher will...

Exercise III

Roots, Prefixes, and Suffixes

Study the entries and answer the questions that follow.

The roots *liber* and *liver* mean "free."
The root *soph* means "wise."
The root *men* means "to think."

1. Using *literal* translations as guidance, define the following words without using a dictionary:

   A. philosophy   D. liberty
   B. sophomore   E. liberate
   C. mental   F. demented

2. A person who has lived a complex life and gathered wisdom might be described as _____.

3. List as many words as you can think of that contain the roots *liber*, *liver*, or *men*.

Exercise IV

Inference

Complete the sentence by inferring information about the italicized word from its context.

1. If someone has an *affliction* that affects his or her legs, then that person might…

2. Pirates might hide their *cache* of stolen goods so that…

3. A security camera might be designed to *oscillate* in order to…

> ## Exercise V

Critical Reading

Below is a pair of reading passages followed by several multiple-choice questions. Carefully read the passages and choose the best answer for each of the questions.

The authors of the following passages discuss the Tunguska event of 1908 in which a strange object exploded with devastating force in the sky over Siberia.

Passage 1

1   In the quest to find answers to unexplained mysteries, there are times to be skeptical and times to be creative. The explanation of the Tunguska explosion of 1908 requires creativity, unless skeptics actually find some physical evidence.

2   The **aphorism**, "truth is stranger than fiction" may be correct, but some puzzles require that we begin with the fiction. On the morning of June 30, 1908, residents near the remote Tunguska River in Siberia witnessed what was doubtlessly the largest, unexplained cataclysmic event of the twentieth century. According to the many eyewitnesses, a blazing, white light—brighter than lightning—streaked across the sky, pulling a tail hundreds of miles in length. Suddenly, while still airborne, the mysterious object detonated over the forest, setting everything beneath it on fire and sending destructive shock waves and heat throughout a 300-mile radius. The description of the ensuing fireball and mushroom cloud most nearly resembles the modern description of a nuclear explosion; however, nuclear weapons weren't even tested until 1945.

3   People had no doubt that something exploded; seismographs around the world detected shock waves that had traveled through thousands of miles of earth, and the sky over Siberia radiated an unnatural glow well into the evening. Unfortunately, due to the isolated region in which the explosion occurred, and the chaotic political state of Russia at the time, no one conducted a formal investigation of the Tunguska event until 1921. Members of the Russian Meteorological Institute found widespread damage, but they found no meteorite impact craters. The detonation had literally leveled the forest more than thirteen miles from the center of the blast, and people living in the region reported that witnesses who didn't die from heat or blast effects died instead from symptoms that indicated radiation poisoning.

4   For more than ninety years, many scientists readily attribute the bizarre explosion to an asteroid or comet that exploded before reaching the earth. Others, including some eyewitnesses, were not so ready to assign such natural explanations to the event; there is no impact crater at the epicenter of the explosion, and investigators discovered no fragments, large or small, of what would have been a massive meteorite.

5   The destruction caused by the Tunguska explosion is commensurate with the effects of a forty-megaton nuclear explosion—that's 1,000 times more powerful than the Hiroshima bomb. In theory, meteorites could indeed cause the massive degree of destruction, but no one is sure why (or if) a meteoroid would detonate before striking the ground.

6   The exploding comet theory is quickly gaining credibility as an explanation because a comet made up of ice and dust would not necessarily leave the evidence required to confirm the composition of the object; however, the comet theory neglects the vast thermal destruction and the apparent radiation effects of the explosion.

7   Some Tunguska theorists offer an antimatter-annihilation as an explanation. Antimatter in sufficient quantity might yield an explosion resembling that of nuclear origin, complete with the radiation effects; however, few can explain how antimatter would exist—let alone travel—throughout our galaxy without being annihilated well before reaching Earth.

8   To many, the antimatter theory might be more credible than the final alternative: a UFO—a spacecraft or missile of extraterrestrial origin—exploded over Tunguska. The craft would have to have been large, of course, to cause such devastation, but without physical evidence of meteors, comets, or an antimatter annihilation, investigators cannot write off such a theory.

9   A century has passed since the Tunguska explosion. It is time to solve the mystery before the event occurs again, but this time in a populated area. The threat of meteorites and other extraterrestrial bodies striking Earth is a growing concern for humanity; we must account for such **afflictions** in this new millennium of human existence. The next Tunguska, whether caused by meteorites, antimatter, or even UFOs, might not be so forgiving as to strike in one of the most desolate areas of the planet. If Tunguska was the product of an asteroid, then we need to prove it and create an appropriate means of defense. If Tunguska was something more complicated than an asteroid, which is quite possible, then we've a lot of reading to do and technology to develop.

Passage 2

1   An unparalleled event occurred in the skies over remote Siberia shortly after 7:00 am on June 30, 1908. Witnesses for miles around, including passengers on a distant train, watched in awe as a blinding white object streaked across the sky for several seconds before exploding in a fireball that would be incomparable for another thirty-seven years, when the atom bomb made its first appearance. The explosion flattened every tree in the forest as far as forty miles from the blast, and simple mountaineers watched as homes, plants, and livestock burst into flames from a rapid surge of intense heat. Inhabitants close to the explosion were thrown through the air like rag dolls, and some of them died as a result of broken bones, severe burns, or a strange sickness that ensued in the following days. Immediately after the blast, rocks rained upon the countryside and dust filled the air, as though a volcano had erupted. A column of fire, perhaps a mile in width, lit the sky well into the evening. Most witnesses had no idea what had just happened; unfortunately, no one was able to offer them a theory until thirteen years later, when the political climate of Russia finally allowed scientists to make the trek to Tunguska. Expecting to find the barely **palpable** evidence of a relatively common meteorite strike, the scientists were surprised to find no impact crater or meteorite pieces; however, that is not sufficient evidence to dismiss the theory that an asteroid or similar object was the cause of the event.

2   For years, several theories have circulated about the source of the explosion. Frenzied theorists speculate about alien attacks, crashing spaceships, antimatter reactions, lightning from the earth, and even a disastrous test of an energy weapon built by the eccentric genius, Nikola Tesla. Serious, ongoing research points not to UFOs or low-probability natural phenomena; instead, most scientists attribute the event to an asteroid or a fragment of a comet, both of which are among the few natural objects capable of such devastating explosions.

3   It is not uncommon, according to scientists, for meteoroids and asteroids to explode in Earth's atmosphere. Many of the stony objects burn up, but with the extreme temperatures and unknown materials involved, it's not inconceivable that many of the objects simply explode. It is easy to imagine that a particularly large body, perhaps an asteroid weighing more than 100,000 tons, would generate tremendous heat and air pressures while traveling at supersonic speeds through the atmosphere. The heat would be so intense that parts of the asteroid would become superheated plasma, essentially creating an unstable, falling bomb. Extreme air pressures, combined with unstable, superheated compounds, could certainly create the necessary conditions for the object to explode.

4   The comet or asteroid that exploded over Tunguska left little evidence on the scene because it disintegrated upon detonation, spreading materials throughout the atmosphere for hundreds of miles around. How much intact material would remain from a relatively small object in a blast equivalent to that of the largest known thermonuclear weapons? Little, if any.

5   In recent years, researchers have compared the dust at the Tunguska site to the dust found in Antarctica that is known to be from meteorite impacts. The samples are very similar in

composition. Scientists also report finding particles imbedded in trees around the site. The particles, they report, are similar to meteorites in composition.

6   It is only a matter of time before the scientific community gathers enough data to prove that the Tunguska explosion was the result of an asteroid or a comet; however, even when that day arrives, irrational skeptics and paranoid green-man watchers will continue to **oscillate** with theories of exploding warp drives or rare, theoretical, natural phenomena. Perhaps in the future, their day will come and they will have license to say they told us so. Until then, though, we must understand Tunguska as the product of a big rock.

1A. The overall tone of the first passage is best described as
    A.   concerned.
    B.   optimistic.
    C.   scientific.
    D.   apologetic.
    E.   timid.

1B. The correct answer to question 1A applies primarily to a single topic from passage 1. That single topic is
    A.   improperly trained scientists.
    B.   another Tunguska event.
    C.   the resilience of humankind.
    D.   an obvious government conspiracy.
    E.   difficulties caused by the Russian government.

2A. According to the first passage, where was the object when it exploded?
    A.   approximately 300 feet above the ground
    B.   approximately 300 miles up
    C.   in the air, over the forest
    D.   between two large clouds
    E.   just above the forest floor

2B. Which detail about the blast area supports your answer to question 2A?
    A.   discovery of meteorite fragments
    B.   confirmed reports of radiation poisoning
    C.   absence of an impact crater
    D.   recent comet sightings
    E.   the fire

3A. According to the first passage, the explosion could not have been an atomic blast because
    A.   people had no means of propulsion for nuclear weapons in 1908.
    B.   there were no radiation effects among the witnesses.
    C.   the treaty banning the use of atomic weapons had been signed.
    D.   the Tunguska event predates nuclear testing by nearly forty years.
    E.   the Russian Meteorological Institute controlled the only atomic bomb.

3B. Choose the line from passage 1 that provides evidence for your answer to question 3A.
   A.   "People had no doubt that something exploded"
   B.   "nuclear weapons weren't even tested until 1945"
   C.   "but they found no meteorite impact craters"
   D.   "meteorites could indeed cause the massive degree of destruction"
   E.   "1,000 times more powerful than the Hiroshima bomb"

4A. As used in paragraph 3 of the first passage, *seismograph* refers to an instrument that
   A.   alerts people to incoming meteorites.
   B.   detects variances in light.
   C.   receives worldwide messages.
   D.   detects movement of the ground.
   E.   measures electromagnetic pulse.

4B. The root *graph* means "writing," which suggests that the instrument in question 4A
   records information visually. Based on your answer to question 4A, the prefix *seismo–*
   probably means
   A.   meteor.
   B.   destruction.
   C.   volcano.
   D.   radiation.
   E.   earthquake.

5.   Why, according to the first passage, must humans develop technology?
   A.   to defend the planet from extraterrestrial threats
   B.   to better understand the properties of antimatter
   C.   to study harmful effects of radiation
   D.   to make contact with the aliens who possibly attacked Siberia
   E.   to prepare for future explosions in outer space

6A. According to paragraph 2 in the second passage, which two groups offer explanations
   of the Tunguska explosion?
   A.   mad scientists and contemporary architects
   B.   the Russian Meteorological Institute and the U.S. Department of State
   C.   witnesses to the explosion and people on the train
   D.   educated workers and local physicians
   E.   overzealous thinkers and real scientists

6B. For your answer to question 6A to be correct, the word *speculate* must mean
   A.   "to argue endlessly."
   B.   "to suppose as true."
   C.   "to research."
   D.   "to reject on principle."
   E.   "to cause fear."

7A. Which of the following best describes the purpose of passage 2?
    A.   to disprove alternative theories of the Tunguska explosion
    B.   to inform readers about new evidence in the Tunguska mystery
    C.   to respond to the author of the first passage
    D.   to support the theory that an asteroid or comet caused the Tunguska event
    E.   to inform readers about the actual Tunguska event

7B. According to the second passage, which of the following is the most sensible theory of the Tunguska explosion?
    A.   Earth was attacked by an alien weapon.
    B.   The explosion was simply a natural phenomenon.
    C.   A comet exploded over the area.
    D.   Tesla conducted a failed test of an energy weapon.
    E.   An antimatter annihilation caused the detonation.

8A. According to the second passage, which of the following would be categorized as low-probability natural phenomenon?
    A.   the explosion of an energy weapon
    B.   lightning coming from the earth
    C.   a brush fire
    D.   a meteorite
    E.   an alien torpedo strike

8B. Passages 1 and 2 contradict each other in which detail of the explosion (passage 1, paragraph 5; passage 2, paragraph 3)?
    A.   the extreme force of the blast
    B.   how the detonation affected the water supply
    C.   the probability of meteors exploding in the air
    D.   the size of the exploding object
    E.   whether the detonation occurred on the ground or in the air

9A. Which of the following best describes the use of the term *skeptic* in both passages?
    A.   *Skeptic* has a negative connotation in passage 1, and it has a positive connotation in passage 2.
    B.   Passage 1 describes skeptics as people who accept simple explanations; passage 2 describes skeptics as people who refuse to accept simple explanations.
    C.   Both passages suggest that skeptics are people who refuse to accept unconventional explanations of strange events.
    D.   Both passages suggest that skeptics are people who refuse to accept traditional explanations of strange events.
    E.   Passage 2 describes skeptics as real scientists, while passage 1 describes skeptics as fanatics.

9B. From your answer to question 9A, you can infer that
    A. a single author wrote both passages.
    B. the authors of both passages would agree on what the next action should be in solving the Tunguska mystery.
    C. Tunguska is most likely the result of a manmade accident.
    D. people might use contradicting definitions for the same word.
    E. humans will never understand the cause of the explosion.

10A. Which of the following best describes similarities between the intent of the passages?
    A. Both passages contain a short explanation of antimatter.
    B. Both passages explain the biological effects of radioactivity.
    C. Both passages are intended to frighten readers.
    D. Both passages acknowledge several theories of the event.
    E. Both passages contain enough supporting data to prove their points.

10B. Choose the assertion that reflects opposition between the two passages.
    A. An asteroid or comet was probably the cause of the Tunguska explosion.
    B. The Tunguska explosion occurred in Siberia.
    C. People died as a result of the Tunguska explosion.
    D. The meteorite that landed in Siberia detonated on the ground.
    E. No one conducted a formal investigation of Tunguska until 1921.

Lesson Seventeen

1. **pariah** (pə rī′ ə) *n.* a social outcast
He knew that he would become a *pariah* if anyone saw him in the police car.
syn: exile; outsider   *ant: insider*

2. **fluent** (flōō′ ənt) *adj.* able to express oneself easily and clearly
The spy travels the world with ease because she is *fluent* in four languages.
syn: well-versed   *ant: inept*

3. **cavort** (kə vôrt′) *v.* to leap about in a sprightly manner; to romp
The children *cavorted* with the puppy in the back yard.
syn: frolic; prance; caper

4. **pedagogue** (ped′ ə gog) *n.* a schoolteacher
A single *pedagogue* taught all the children in the rural county.
syn: educator

5. **melee** (mā′ lā) *n.* a noisy, confused fight
By the time the police arrived, the *melee* was over.
syn: skirmish; fracas

6. **ensue** (en sōō′) *v.* to follow as a result
The monkey escaped from the laboratory, and an epidemic *ensued*.
syn: result   *ant: cause*

7. **desecrate** (des′ i krāt) *v.* to damage a holy place; to treat with irreverence
The vandals *desecrated* the little church.
syn: vandalize; violate   *ant: consecrate*

8. **personification** (per son i fi kā′ shən) *n.* a person or thing that represents an idea
The old woman was the very *personification* of greed.

9. **bias** (bī′ əs) *n.* a prejudiced view (either for or against); a preference
The jurors were instructed to review the facts without *bias*.
syn: partiality; favoritism

10. **aloof** (ə lōōf′) *adj.* reserved; distant
The teacher remained *aloof* for a few days after arguing with the principal.
syn: detached; cold; remote   *ant: warm; friendly*

11. **gyrate**   (jī′ rāt)   *v.*   to rotate or revolve quickly; to spiral
People used to dance together, but now they simply *gyrate* in random patterns.
syn: revolve; whirl

12. **fiat**   (fī′ at)   *n.*   an official order
The dictator's harsh *fiat* turned the rebels into outlaws.
syn: decree; authorization

13. **fidelity**   (fi del′ i tē, fī)   *n.*   faithfulness
The king told his subjects that their *fidelity* would be rewarded.
syn: loyalty; devotion   *ant: treachery*

14. **rambunctious**   (ram bungk′ shəs)   *adj.*   unruly; uncontrollable
The *rambunctious* twins kept the house in an uproar from morning until night.
syn: wild; disorderly; boisterous   *ant: calm; pacific; tranquil*

15. **hilarity**   (hi la′ ri tē)   *n.*   gaiety; joviality
Uncle Harvey's jokes always brought *hilarity* to the family picnics.
syn: mirth; merriment; glee   *ant: sadness; misery*

Exercise I

Words in Context

From the list below, supply the words needed to complete the paragraph. Some words will not be used.

fluent	pariah	ensue	rambunctious
fiat	melee	desecrate	

1. Community outrage _____ when the groundskeeper reported that a group of _____ teenagers had _____ the cemetery.

   "What kind of _____ sinks so low as to destroy that which cannot be defended?" asked the mayor when told of the crime. "These are memorials to our forefathers, our families." The mayor, forced to take some type of action to prevent such outrageous crimes, issued a[n] _____ mandating a curfew on the small town.

From the list below, supply the words needed to complete the paragraph. Some words will not be used.

bias	aloof	pariah	pedagogue
cavort	fluent	hilarity	

2. The aging _____, a teacher for twenty-two years, was _____ enough in adolescent psychology to know that something was wrong with Anne. The girl normally _____ in the halls and laughed with her friends, but she hadn't spoken a word in a week. During class, she remained _____ and stared out the window into a distant field. The teacher's concern was without _____; he genuinely cared about all his students, not just those, like Anne, who made teaching enjoyable.

From the list below, supply the words needed to complete the paragraph. Some words will not be used.

fidelity	hilarity	melee	personification
fiat	gyrate	cavort	

3. Startled by crashing noises coming from the office, Tina ran out of the living room to find her two sons in a _____. Apparently, they were fighting over who was next to spin around in the office chair.

   "You've got hundreds of toys upstairs, and you two fight over who gets to _____ in an office chair?" screamed Tina. "Go play outside—it's a nice day!" As the boys, one six and the other seven, ran into the yard, Tina wondered what would become the next object of conflict. Her boys were the _____ of sibling rivalry— they fought over rights to everything, no matter how silly. The ridiculous disputes were often cause for _____, but too much of it quickly became irritating. Despite the rivalry, Tina didn't question the boys' _____ to each other as brothers; they covered for each other as often as they fought.

Exercise II

Sentence Completion

Complete the sentence in a way that shows you understand the meaning of the italicized vocabulary word.

1. The *hilarity* of the celebration was interrupted when...

2. Joe felt like the *pariah* of the class because he...

3. After buying new furniture, Dad warned the *rambunctious* children to...

4. Jan-Tommy is from Norway, but he became *fluent* in English by...

5. The general questioned the *fidelity* of his troops before he ordered them to...

6. Bobby *cavorted* around in the living room until his mom told him that...

7. The company president issued a *fiat* which stated that his employees were to...

8. The *pedagogue* eventually stopped teaching and became the...

9. When the young girl jumped on the table and began to *gyrate* wildly, her mother...

10. Like most action movies, this one featured a big *melee* near the end in which the hero...

11. When Cory began to act very *aloof*, his parents knew that something was wrong because he was usually...

12. Cheering *ensued* when the home team...

13. To eliminate any *bias* from the team selection, judges were chosen from a group of people who had never...

14. Tomb raiders and scavengers *desecrated* the ancient pyramid by...

15. Jerry, who missed the plane that crashed and then bought a winning lottery ticket, is the *personification* of...

Exercise III

Roots, Prefixes, and Suffixes

Study the entries and answer the questions that follow.

The root *tract* means "to draw" or "to dig."
The root *anthro* means "man."
The suffix *–ology* means "the study of."
The suffix *–oid* means "like."

1. Using *literal* translations as guidance, define the following words without using a dictionary:

    A. intractable   D. zoologist
    B. contract   E. spheroid
    C. biology   F. humanoid

2. The study of man is called _____, and a creature with characteristics that resemble those of man is called a[n] _____.

3. A building *contractor* might need to _____ a foundation before beginning construction. You might find yourself drawn to a[n] _____ person.

4. List as many words as you can think of that contain the root *tract* or end with the suffixes *–oid* or *–ology*.

Exercise IV

Inference

Complete the sentence by inferring information about the italicized word from its context.

1. If judges show *bias* in favor of a particular contestant in a beauty pageant, that contestant will probably…

2. The movie villain was described as the *personification* of evil because he…

3. Few people talked to Billy, the *pariah* of the town, because he…

Exercise V

Writing

Here is a writing prompt similar to the one you will find on the writing portion of an assessment test.

Plan and write an essay based on the following statement:

> Lives of great men all remind us
> We can make our lives sublime,
> And, departing, leave behind us
> Footsteps on the sands of time;
>
> Footsteps, that perhaps another,
> Sailing o'er life's solemn main,
> A forlorn and shipwrecked brother,
> Seeing, shall take heart again.
>
> Let us then, be up and doing,
> With a heart for any fate;
> Still achieving, still pursuing,
> Learn to labor and to wait.

–Henry Wadsworth Longfellow (1807-1882), "A Psalm of Life"

Assignment: Do you agree or disagree with Longfellow's philosophy? In an essay, identify and explain the poem's message about living. Explain why it is legitimate or not, and whether you agree or disagree with it. Support your argument with evidence from your knowledge, reading, experience, or observation.

Thesis: Write a *one-sentence* response to the assignment. Make certain this single sentence offers a clear statement of your position.

Example: In "A Psalm of Life," Henry Wadsworth Longfellow implies that the best reason to achieve anything is to inspire future generations, but this is not a satisfactory reason to achieve.

_____

_____

Organizational Plan: List at least three subtopics you will use to support your main idea. This list is your outline.

1. _____

2. _____

3. _____

Draft: Following your outline, write a good first draft of your essay. Remember to support all your points with examples, facts, references to reading, etc.

Review and Revise: Exchange essays with a classmate. Using the scoring guide for Word Choice on page 255, score your partner's essay (while he or she scores yours). Focus on word choice and the use of language conventions. If necessary, rewrite your essay to improve word choice and/or your use of language.

Exercise VI

English Practice

Identifying Sentence Errors

Identify the grammatical error in each of the following sentences. If the sentence contains no error, select answer choice E.

1. <u>None of the friends</u> in the <u>lower apartment</u> <u>was injured</u> when the <u>waterbed burst</u>
       (A)   (B)   (C)   (D)
   through the ceiling.   <u>No error</u>
                                     (E)

2. <u>Bring with you</u> only <u>necessary</u> <u>clothing, leave</u> your blankets
       (A)   (B)   (C)
   <u>at home</u>.   <u>No error</u>
    (D)   (E)

3. <u>Today, less than</u> 25 million Americans <u>work in the fields</u> to produce
    (A)   (B)   (C)
   <u>fruits and vegetables.</u>   <u>No error</u>
         (D)   (E)

4. When I <u>told you</u> I <u>had no plans</u> for the weekend, I did not <u>mean to infer</u> that
        (A)   (B)   (C)
   <u>I didn't want to plan</u> anything.   <u>No error</u>
        (D)   (E)

5. <u>Although</u> she admits <u>she has never seen</u> one, my <u>Aunt Margaret says</u> she
    (A)   (B)   (C)
   <u>believes in angles</u> anyway.   <u>No error</u>
      (D)   (E)

Improving Sentences

The underlined portion of each sentence below contains some flaw. Select the answer choice that best corrects the flaw.

6. Doug took a nasty blow to the head, <u>but may be his condition will improve</u> after he gets a few hours of rest.
   A. but may be his condition might improve
   B. but maybe a few hours of rest will improve
   C. but maybe his condition will improve
   D. but his condition will improve
   E. but his condition will maybe improve

7. Anne walked into town hall, made some nasty remarks in front of the mayor, <u>and then she rushes right out to the bus.</u>
   A. then rushes out the door and right onto the bus.
   B. and then rushed right out to the bus.
   C. and the bus was waiting outside, so she jumps on it.
   D. so Anne rushes out and gets on the bus.
   E. then she was rushed right out to the bus.

8. Some women like to wear short skirts, <u>but long dresses are preferred by others.</u>
   A. whereas some do not prefer short skirts.
   B. but sometimes they only wear long dresses.
   C. long dresses are worn by others.
   D. and others are long-dress wearers.
   E. but others prefer long dresses.

9. <u>If our radio is turned on and loud all the time and we don't do our homework properly.</u>
   A. If our radio is turned on and loud all the time, we don't do our homework properly.
   B. Our homework isn't done properly if the radio is too loud, and it's on all the time.
   C. If our radio is on all the time, and turned up too loud, and we don't do our homework properly.
   D. We don't do our homework properly, and the radio is on all the time and it's too loud.
   E. We have the radio on all the time and up too loud if we don't do our homework properly.

10. <u>Tiffany and Jeremy fought over the remote control while I tried to read a book noisily.</u>
    A. The remote control was fought over noisily by Jeremy and Tiffany while I tried to read a book.
    B. Tiffany and Jeremy fought over the remote control noisily; while I tried to read a book.
    C. Tiffany and Jeremy fought over the remote control noisily at the same time, I tried to read a book.
    D. Tiffany and Jeremy fought noisily over the remote control while I tried to read a book.
    E. While Tiffany and Jeremy fought over the remote control; I tried to read a book.

Lesson Eighteen

1. **genocide** (je′ nə sīd)   *n.*   the deliberate destruction of a group of people
   The Nazi *genocide* of millions of Jewish people was a dark time in world history.

2. **resign** (ri zīn′)   *v.*   to accept as inevitable; to give up
   Knowing that her drug habit was slowly killing her, she *resigned* herself to quitting by the first of the year.
   syn: submit   *ant: resist; deny*

3. **predilection** (pre dəl ek′ shən)   *n.*   a preference toward someone
   or something
   His *predilection* for fast food helped to clog his arteries at an early age.
   syn: preference; partiality; penchant   *ant: aversion; hatred*

4. **faux** (fō)   *adj.*   artificial; false; not genuine
   The *faux*-marble countertop is really made of cheap plastic.
   syn: fake; imitation   *ant: authentic; true*

5. **foray** (fôr′ ā)   *n.*   a surprise attack, especially into enemy territory; a journey
   The Green Berets conducted a *foray* on the enemy fuel depot.
   syn: raid; incursion

6. **conjecture** (kən jek′ chər)   *n.*   a judgment or opinion based on little or
   questionable evidence
   The defense attorney said that the prosecutor's claims were pure *conjecture*.
   syn: speculation; guesswork   *ant: fact*

7. **allocate** (al′ ə kāt)   *v.*   to distribute, allot, or designate
   The government *allocated* the funds for victims of natural disasters.
   syn: apportion; assign

8. **gratis** (gra′ təs)   *adv., adj.*   free; without charge
   Tom could have earned ten dollars an hour, but he volunteered to work *gratis*.

9. **materialistic** (mə tēr ē əl is′ tik)   *adj.*   wanting material possessions
   The *materialistic* man cared only about keeping up with his neighbors.
                                                      ant: altruistic

10. **belabor** (bi la′ bər)   *v.*   to work at something beyond practicality; to overstress
    Mom constantly *belabored* the fact that our grades would have to get us through college because her paycheck couldn't.
    syn: stress; overdo   *ant: disregard; ignore*

11. **progeny** (prä´ jə nē)   *n.*   offspring; children
Only a few of the sea turtle's *progeny* will survive predators and live to adulthood.
syn: descendents; young   *ant: ancestors*

12. **quintessential** (kwin tə sen´ shəl)   *adj.*   the most typical; ideal
Johann Sebastian Bach was the *quintessential* Baroque composer.
syn: model; standard

13. **rudimentary** (rōō də men´ tə rē)   *adj.*   basic; not refined or well developed
She claimed to be a great critic despite only a *rudimentary* understanding of literature.
syn: elementary; undeveloped   *ant: refined; sophisticated*

14. **monolithic** (mä nə lith´ ik)   *adj.*   massive, uniform, and solid
The *monolithic* monument, made of pure granite, weighed one million tons.

15. **manifesto** (ma nə fes´ tō)   *n.*   a public declaration of policies or intentions
The conservation group's *manifesto* declared that its members were opponents of any industries that pollute the enviroment.
syn: proclamation

Exercise I

Words in Context

From the list below, supply the words needed to complete the paragraph. Some words will not be used.

rudimentary	**predilection**	**allocate**	**monolithic**
conjecture	**quintessential**	**belabor**	

1. Horace attributes his career as a skyscraper window-washer to his _____ for being in high places. He also says that the _____ rule of the trade is not, "Don't look down," but, "Always attach your safety harness." Anyone with a[n] _____ knowledge of climbing knows that equipment fails and people fall if they haven't taken any precautions.

    "I can't _____ the point enough," said Horace. "Safety, safety, safety." After the brief interview, Horace climbed back into his elevator scaffold and began the ascent back to the forty-first story of the _____ building that he was cleaning this week.

From the list below, supply the words needed to complete the paragraph. Some words will not be used.

gratis	**progeny**	**genocide**	**monolithic**
materialistic	**allocate**	**faux**	

2. Cindy was not _____, but she still refused to buy the _____ leather furniture; she really believed that having plastic furniture was tacky. When she _____ a large portion of her savings to purchasing things for her new home, she promised herself to buy only items that would retain some of their intrinsic, if not monetary, value. The ornate furnishings that she ultimately selected would last for a long time, perhaps long enough for her _____ to enjoy. After making the substantial purchase, Cindy was happy to learn the store would deliver the items to her home _____.

From the list below, supply the words needed to complete the paragraph. Some words will not be used.

resign	**genocide**	**foray**	**quintessential**
faux	**conjecture**	**manifesto**	

3. Few outsiders knew for sure the condition of the city in the days following the violent uprising, but most _____ portrayed a place of rampant looting and lawlessness after the rebels' _____ into the capital city. Winston, the nearest correspondent, traveled to the city to report the situation, and what he found shocked him. Poor-quality copies of the revolutionaries' _____ hung on bullet-riddled walls. Orphaned children and distraught mothers roamed the streets as remnants of the near-_____ that had occurred in the weeks leading to the uprising. Most of the combatants _____ themselves to simple survival, considering themselves lucky that food and water were in good supply for the moment.

Exercise II

Sentence Completion

Complete the sentence in a way that shows you understand the meaning of the italicized vocabulary word.

1. After the accident, the *materialistic* man worried only about…

2. The ballerina *resigned* herself to practicing an extra two hours a night for the next month because…

3. You will certainly see *monolithic* structures if you go…

4. The family *allocated* a portion of its income for…

5. Every time the kids prepared to go boating, Dad *belabored* them with the importance of…

6. The world accused the ruler of *genocide* for ordering his army to…

7. The political party released a *manifesto* that described…

8. Critics complained that the new book was mostly *conjecture* because it…

9. Olivia escaped the destitute nation so that her *progeny* might…

10. Sam had a *predilection* for living in the mountains, so he…

11. Yvonne's *rudimentary* knowledge of auto repair was not enough for her to…

12. During the Vikings' *foray*, the surprised villagers…

13. The *quintessential* teenager spends lots of time…

14. The *faux* mink coat is actually…

15. The technology billionaire provided *gratis* medical care to…

Exercise III

Roots, Prefixes, and Suffixes

Study the entries and answer the questions that follow.

The roots *ped* and *pod* mean "foot."
The root *phob* means "fear."
The root *port* means "to carry" or "bring."

1. Using *literal* translations as guidance, define the following words without using a dictionary:

    A. import
    B. transport
    C. impede

    D. report
    E. podiatrist
    F. hydrophobia

2. A _____ creature has two legs, a stand with three legs is called a[n] _____, and an animal with four legs is called a[n] _____.

3. If you are afraid of feet, then you might be said to have _____. Someone who fears being in an enclosed space, called a *claustrum* in Latin, is said to have _____.

4. List as many words as you can think of that contain the roots *ped*, *pod*, or *port*.

Exercise IV

Inference

Complete the sentence by inferring information about the italicized word from its context.

1. To a *materialistic* person, owning an expensive car might be more important than…

2. The *faux* brick paneling is cheaper than real brick, but it…

3. The scientist's theory was mostly *conjecture*, so the board of directors…

Exercise V

Critical Reading

Below is a reading passage followed by several multiple-choice questions. Carefully read the passage and choose the best answer for each of the questions.

The following passage is an adapted excerpt from Chapter 3 of The Comic History of the United States, *by Edgar "Bill" Nye. A famous American humorist at the time, Nye summarizes some of the "facts" and legends of early European colonization in America.*

This chapter is given up almost wholly to facts. It deals largely with the beginning of the thirteen original colonies from which sprang the Republic, the operation of which now gives so many thousands of men in-door employment four years at a time, thus relieving the penitentiaries and throwing more kindergarten statesmen to the front.

5　　It was during this epoch that the Cavaliers landed in Virginia and the Puritans in Massachusetts; the latter lived on maple sugar and armed prayer, while the former saluted his cow, and, with bared head, milked her with his hat in one hand and his life in the other.

Immigration now began to increase along the coast. The Mayflower began to bring over vast quantities of antique furniture, mostly hall-clocks for future sales. Hanging them on spars and masts

10　during rough weather easily accounts for the fact that none of them have ever been known to go.

The Puritans now began to barter with the Indians, swapping square black bottles of liquid hell for farms in Massachusetts and additions to log towns. Dried apples and schools began to make their appearance. The low retreating forehead of the codfish began to be seen at the stores, and virtue began to break out among the Indians after death.

15　　Virginia, however, deserves mention here on the start. This colony was poorly prepared to tote wood and sleep out-of-doors, as the people were all gents by birth. They had no families, but came to Virginia to obtain fortunes and return to the city of New York in September. The climate was unhealthy, and before the first autumn, says Sir William Kronk, from whom I quote, "ye greater numberr of them hade perished of a great Miserrie in the Side and for lacke of Food, for

20　at thatte time the Crosse betwene the wilde hyena and the common hogge of the Holy Lande, and since called the Razor Backe Hogge, had not been made, and so many of the courtiers dyede."

John Smith saved the colony. He was one of the best Smiths that ever came to this country, which is as large an encomium as a man cares to travel with. He would have saved the life of Pocahontas, an Indian girl who also belonged to the gentry of their tribe, but she saw at once

25　that it would be a point for her to save him, so after a month's rehearsal with her father as villain, with Smith's part taken by a chunk of blue-gum wood, they succeeded in getting this little curtain-raiser to perfection.

Pocahontas was afterwards married, if the author's memory does not fail him, to John Rolfe. Pocahontas was not beautiful, but many good people sprang from her. She never touched

30　them. Her husband sprang from her also just in time. The way she jumped from a clay-eating crowd into the bosom of the English aristocracy by this dramatic ruse was worthy of a greater recognition than merely to figure among the makers of smoking-tobacco with fancy wrappers, when she never had a fancy wrapper in her life.

Smith was captured once by the Indians, and, instead of telling them that he was by birth a

35　gent, he gave them a course of lectures on the use of the compass and how to learn where one is at. Thus one after another the Indians went away. I often wonder why the lecture is not used more as a means of escape from hostile people.

By writing a letter and getting a reply to it, he made another hit. He now became a great man among the Indians; and to kill a dog and fail to invite Smith to the symposium was considered as vulgar as it

40　is now to rest the arctic overshoe on the corner of the dining-table while buckling or unbuckling it.

Smith fell into the hands of Powhatan, the Croker of his time, and narrowly saved his life, as we have seen, through the intervention of Pocahontas.

Smith was now required in England to preside at a dinner given by the Savage Club, and to tell a few stories of life in the Far West.

45   While he was gone the settlement became a prey to disease and famine. Some were killed by the Indians while returning from their club at evening; some became pirates.

    The colony decreased from four hundred and ninety to sixty people, and at last it was moved and seconded that they do now adjourn. They started away from Jamestown without a tear, or hardly anything else, having experienced a very dull time there, funerals being the only

50 relaxation whatever.

    But moving down the bay they met Lord Delaware, the new Governor, with a lot of Christmas-presents and groceries. Jamestown was once more saved, though property still continued low. The company, by the terms of its new charter, became a self-governing institution, and London was only too tickled to get out of the responsibility. It is said that the only genuine

55 humor up to that time heard in London was spent on the jays of Jamestown and the Virginia colony.

1A. Who, according to paragraph 1, receive jobs as a product of the Republic?
    A.   sailors
    B.   Cavaliers
    C.   explorers
    D.   politicians
    E.   teachers

1B. Which word from paragraph 1 directly supports your answer to question 1A?
    A.   statesmen
    B.   colonies
    C.   penitentiaries
    D.   kindergarten
    E.   facts

2A. The best word to describe the author's tone, as it applies to the subject of government, is
    A.   trusting.
    B.   shocked.
    C.   amused.
    D.   outraged.
    E.   mocking.

2B. The author provides details about the men who receive "employment" from the Republic. Which one of the following details about the men *cannot* be found in paragraph 1?
    A.   They enjoy a fixed term of employment.
    B.   They are either inexperienced or criminals.
    C.   The men seek popularity as much as they do wealth.
    D.   They are all convicted lawbreakers.
    E.   They do not have to labor in the fields.

3A. Knowing that the early colonists in America were doomed to meager lives of starvation and despair, what can be inferred about the colonists from the nature of the imports described in paragraph 3?
   A.   They lost one supply ship halfway through the voyage.
   B.   They planned to establish a clockmaking industry.
   C.   The settlers had a poor sense of priorities.
   D.   They could not afford modern furniture.
   E.   They had disdain for the weather of Massachusetts.

3B. Grandfather clocks ("hall clocks"), were not invented until 1700, eighty years after the *Mayflower's* first voyage with the Puritans. If this anachronism is a fact, then the details of paragraph 3
   A.   warn the reader that the passage contains invented "facts."
   B.   show the contrast between the Puritans and the Native Americans.
   C.   establish the author's reason for writing the essay.
   D.   show why the Puritans wanted so many clocks.
   E.   are used to establish an argument against colonization.

4A. Which detail of paragraph 2 best suggests that the Cavaliers supported the king?
   A.   the hat
   B.   the epoch
   C.   the *Mayflower*
   D.   the salute
   E.   maple sugar

4B. The diet of the Puritans suggests that they depended on which means of staying alive, according to paragraph 2?
   A.   farming and syrup
   B.   milk and weapons
   C.   trading and sailing
   D.   respect and agriculture
   E.   religion and defense

4C. According to the author, the Cavaliers fared poorly in Virginia mainly because
   A.   they had to sleep outside.
   B.   the settlers were aristocrats.
   C.   they were too young.
   D.   they had no families.
   E.   they sought fortunes.

5A. As it is used in line 23, the word *encomium* most nearly means
   A.   burden.
   B.   responsibility.
   C.   shame.
   D.   horror.
   E.   commendation.

5B. Which one of the following details provides the best evidence for your answer to question 5A?
   A. The word is necessary for the author's joke to work.
   B. The Native Americans do not speak Latin.
   C. Very few Smiths immigrate to America.
   D. The staged rescue tricks John Smith.
   E. The word refers to the phrase, "one of the best."

6A. According to paragraph 6, Pocahontas was
   A. an abandoned member of her tribe.
   B. difficult to get along with.
   C. at odds with her father.
   D. a member of the upper class in her culture.
   E. a martyr for the cause of peace.

6B. Based on your answer to question 6A, the word *gentry* as it appears in paragraph 6 is synonymous with
   A. structure.
   B. church.
   C. banished.
   D. children.
   E. nobility.

7A. According to paragraph 6, John Smith did not save Pocahontas because
   A. he had no support from the colony.
   B. she was not in any danger.
   C. he was imprisoned by her father.
   D. it was against the law for him to do so.
   E. she refused to leave her village.

7B. Which words or phrases from the passage suggest that the legend of Pocahontas's rescue of John Smith is actually a fabrication?
   A. unhealthy, villain, great man
   B. perfection, compass, by birth
   C. rehearsal, curtain-raiser, dramatic ruse
   D. another hit, retreating forehead, lectures
   E. buckling, greater recognition, vulgar

8A. As it is used in line 39, the word *symposium* most nearly means
   A. gathering.
   B. speech.
   C. experiment.
   D. zone.
   E. fight.

8B. The correct answer to question 8A is most probable because
   A. *symposium* is used in a context of science.
   B. it is customary for the guest to prepare the dog.
   C. John Smith had proven his communication abilities.
   D. the *symposium* involves an invitation and a feast.
   E. no one expected John Smith to attend the *symposium*.

9A. According to lines 34-46, how many times was John Smith captured by the Native Americans?
   A. 1
   B. 2
   C. 3
   D. 4
   E. 5

9B. In the chronology of the passage, Pocahontas marries John Rolfe
   A. before she saves John Smith.
   B. after Jamestown is abandoned.
   C. when Puritans made contact with Native Americans.
   D. after she saves John Smith.
   E. after the arrival of the new governor.

10A. Choose the most accurate description of the academic content of the passage.
   A. logical and thoughtful
   B. sympathetic and precise
   C. dismissive and erratic
   D. intellectual and troubled
   E. consistent and reliable

10B. Which choice identifies a topic which the author does *not* ridicule?
   A. the upper class
   B. self-promotion
   C. victims of harsh conditions
   D. exploited native populations
   E. seafaring people

Vocabulary Power Plus for College and Career Readiness

LEVEL

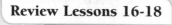

Review Lessons 16-18

Exercise I

Inferences

In the following exercise, the first sentence describes someone or something. Infer information from the first sentence, and then choose the word from the Word Bank that best completes the second sentence.

rudimentary	bias	quintessential	fidelity
impermeable	palpable	conjecture	imperturbable

1. If the queen thought anyone on her court was working against her, then the suspected offender usually disappeared quietly, in the night.

   From this sentence, we can infer that _____ to the queen was not optional, but mandatory.

2. The toddler yanked on the hound dog's ears, sat on his back, and inadvertently poked the dog's eyes, but the old dog never once nipped at the little girl.

   From this sentence, we can infer that the _____ dog is very good with young children.

3. Stranded on the island, the professor used a stick of bamboo surrounded by twelve evenly spaced pebbles in order to determine the time of day, at least when the sun was shining.

   From this sentence, we can infer that the professor made a[n] _____ clock.

4. The steel containers are designed to isolate the deadly virus from the environment.

   From this sentence, we can infer that the containers are _____.

5. The biologist had great theories, but never attempted to prove them through experiments.

   From this sentence, we can infer that the biologist's ideas were merely _____.

Exercise II

Related Words

Some of the vocabulary words from Lessons 16 through 18 have related meanings. Complete the following sentences by choosing the word that best fits the context, based on information you infer from the use of the italicized word. Some word pairs will be antonyms, some will be synonyms, and some will simply be words often used in the same context.

1. The foreman at the lumber mill *belabored* employees about the need for personal safety equipment such as goggles and hardhats, but his _____ enforcement of equipment maintenance rendered some of the machinery hazardous.
   A. lax
   B. palpable
   C. smug
   D. gaunt
   E. fluent

2. The polar bear found the arctic surveyor's buried food _____ and enjoyed a tasty dinner, *gratis*.
   A. bias
   B. progeny
   C. foible
   D. cache
   E. pariah

3. While the _____ gathered newspapers to stuff into his coat for extra insulation against the cold, a *materialistic* tenant in the apartment above the alley threw his unfashionable jackets and gloves into the trash bin.
   A. paean
   B. pedagogue
   C. mendicant
   D. progeny
   E. pariah

4. In his final days, the insane emperor released a *manifesto* detailing his demands for allegiance and tribute and ending with a _____ by which the state claimed ownership of all personal property and wealth.
   A. genocide
   B. cache
   C. melee
   D. conjecture
   E. fiat

5. Roger, a car enthusiast, felt that the cheap-looking *faux* wood dashboard _____ what otherwise would have been a beautiful reproduction of a classic luxury car.
    A. ensued
    B. belabored
    C. daubed
    D. desecrated
    E. garbled

6. A *palpable* fear left some of the torpedo plane pilots dazed, momentarily, as the _____ steel battleship—the largest in the enemy fleet—rose above the horizon.
    A. faux
    B. palpable
    C. monolithic
    D. aloof
    E. fallible

7. Even though the judge has a[n] _____ for the defendant's professional football team, he must not show any *bias* in his verdict.
    A. aplomb
    B. predilection
    C. paean
    D. progeny
    E. affliction

8. The new book quickly became controversial because it was essentially a _____ to a much-hated historical *pariah* who reigned through terror and genocide.
    A. paean
    B. queue
    C. predilection
    D. foray
    E. modicum

9. Buy a pair of high quality *impermeable* boots if your job is sewer inspector, or plenty of disgust will _____.
    A. oust
    B. ensue
    C. imbue
    D. resign
    E. oscillate

10. Uncle Joe was wounded during a *melee* and firefight in the war when his platoon got ambushed during a[n] _____ into enemy territory.
    A. conjecture
    B. foray
    C. pariah
    D. manifesto
    E. queue

Exercise III

Deeper Meanings

Choose a word to replace the italicized word in each sentence. All of the possible choices for each sentence have similar definitions, but the correct answer will have a connotation that best suits the context. For example, the words "delete," "destroy," and "obliterate" all mean "to remove or wipe out," but no one would ever say, "I destroyed the name from the document." The correct choice will be the word that has the best specific meaning and does not render the sentence awkward in tone or content. When choices seem close, look for a clue in the context that makes one choice better than the other.

Note that the correct answer is not always the primary vocabulary word from the lesson.

tragedy	vandalized	rudimentary	outcast
exiled	affliction	undeveloped	loner
ousted	situation	soiled	

1. The city council immediately *removed* the treasurer after he was caught stealing funds from city accounts.

    Better word: _____

2. Kerry had changed schools several times already and was used to being a[n] *pariah* for a few weeks until he had time to make new friends.

    Better word: _____

3. Malaria, a major *problem* in tropical regions, causes many thousands of deaths around the world each year.

    Better word: _____

4. The archaeologists thought they had found a simple ancient vase, but were shocked to see that the vessel was, in fact, a[n] *raw* battery, crafted in a time before electricity was understood.

    Better word: _____

5. Steve accidentally *desecrated* the brand new couch when he fell asleep with a full cup of grape juice in his hand.

    Better word: _____

Exercise IV

Crossword Puzzle

Use the clues to complete the crossword puzzle. The answers consist of vocabulary words from Lessons 16 through 18.

Across

5. so real you can taste it
6. search and destroy mission
10. a lean toward one side
12. on the house
14. waterproof
15. faithfulness
16. the kids
17. really good at
18. prance around

Down

1. teacher
2. phony
3. no rules
4. deal out
7. kick out
8. funny times
9. follow
11. official decree
13. make disappear

Exercise V

Subject Prompts

Here is a writing prompt similar to the one you will find on the writing portion of an assessment test. Follow the instructions below and write a brief, efficient essay.

Math, language, and science will always be the core of education, but that core curriculum accounts for only a proportion of the classes you take in high school. At one time in America, the core curriculum included certain practical courses such as wood and metal shop, home economics, and typing, among others.

If you could add three courses to the core curriculum, what would they be, and why? Consider the skills that you think would be valuable to you one day, whether during your education, or twenty years from now. Your suggestions might even include activities you enjoy, or skills that require more practical experience than traditional textbooks and quizzes.

Your essay should be in the form of a letter to the Department of Education. Be sure to explain why each of your three choices would be valuable and legitimate additions to the curriculum. Your suggestions might be interesting to you, but you have to sell your ideas to a school board.

Thesis: Write a *one-sentence* response to the assignment. Make certain this single sentence offers a clear statement of your position.

Example: Courses that allow students to be self-reliant are especially important, and the first to add to a curriculum should be basic auto repair.

_____

_____

Organizational Plan: List at least three subtopics you will use to support your main idea. This list is your outline.

1. _____

2. _____

3. _____

Draft: Following your outline, write a good first draft of your essay. Remember to support all your points with examples, facts, references to reading, etc.

Review and Revise: Exchange essays with a classmate. Using the scoring guide for Organization on page 251, score your partner's essay (while he or she scores yours). Focus on the organizational plan and the use of language conventions. If necessary, rewrite your essay to improve the organizational plan and/or your use of language.

Vocabulary Power Plus for College and Career Readiness

Lesson Nineteen

1. **tantamount** (tan´ tə maunt) *adj.* of essentially equal value or significance
   To the professor, using notes during tests is *tantamount* to cheating.
   syn: *equivalent; commensurate*   ant: *incomparable*

2. **subversive** (sub vər´ siv) *adj.* in opposition to authority or government
   The most *subversive* idea in the controversial book was that citizens should no longer pay income taxes.
   syn: *dissident; rebellious*   ant: *loyal*

3. **conducive** (kən dōō´ siv) *adj.* tending to cause or bring about
   Job dissatisfaction is often *conducive* to high levels of stress.
   syn: *contributive*

4. **amenable** (ə mē´ nə bəl) *adj.* agreeable; responsive to suggestion or advice
   The *amenable* boss listened to and acted upon the workers' complaints.
   syn: *responsive; tractable*   ant: *inflexible*

5. **stricture** (strik´ chər) *n.* a restraint or limit
   Faced with overpopulation, the government enacted harsh *strictures* on immigration.
   syn: *constraints; limitations*

6. **sedentary** (sed´ ən ter ē) *adj.* characterized by or requiring sitting; motionless
   The regional salesman sought a *sedentary* job that did not require driving or heavy lifting every day.
   syn: *inactive*

7. **influx** (in´ fluks) *n.* an inward flow
   Thanks to wise investing, Meg had a steady *influx* of money in her bank account.
   ant: *outflow*

8. **rigorous** (ri´ gə rəs) *adj.* severe; relentless; harsh
   Hiram completed *rigorous* training to prepare for his trek to the summit of Mount Everest.
   syn: *arduous; grueling*   ant: *easy; painless*

9. **patina** (pə tē´ nə) *n.* a sheen on a surface resulting from age or use
   The *patina* on the antique lamp gave the item character but reduced its value.

10. **placebo** (pla sē´ bō) *n.* a fake drug used in the testing of medication
    Half of the test subjects ingested the real drug, and the other half took *placebos*.

11. **junta**   (hun´ tə)   *n.*   a military group ruling a country after seizing power
    After the revolution, a *junta* governed the island nation until elections were held.

12. **pinnacle**   (pi´ ni kəl)   *n.*   a peak or climax
    The *pinnacle* of her career was her two-month trip to Russia.
    syn: summit; apex   *ant: nadir*

13. **mollify**   (mä´ lə fī)   *v.*   to reduce, soothe, or calm
    Amber attempted to *mollify* the baby by singing her a song.
    syn: placate; pacify   *ant: enrage*

14. **perjury**   (pər´ jə rē)   *n.*   lying under oath
    The gangster was charged with *perjury* for implicating an innocent man in the crime.

15. **plaintive**   (plān´ tiv)   *adj.*   expressing sorrow; mournful
    The *plaintive* poem brought tears to her eyes.
    syn: melancholic   *ant: joyful*

Exercise I

Words in Context

From the list below, supply the words needed to complete the paragraph. Some words will not be used.

influx	**pinnacle**	**sedentary**	**junta**
conducive	**rigorous**	**stricture**	

1. Heather knew that she would need to impose some _____ on her eating habits in order to comply with her _____ training regimen in the weeks before the marathon. Timing was crucial; in order to place well, Heather would need to reach the _____ of her fitness on the day of the race. Several days of rest before the race will be _____ to her winning, but until that time, no one would be able to regard Heather as _____; if she's not sleeping, she will be running.

From the list below, supply the words needed to complete the paragraph. Some words will not be used.

perjury	**rigorous**	**influx**	**plaintive**
amenable	**mollify**	**tantamount**	

2. The steady _____ of observers continued until every seat in the courtroom was filled. Everyone watched the famous defendant, who appeared to be _____ to what was being said as she nodded in affirmation to each whisper from her lawyer. While on the stand, the defendant had a[n] _____ look as she described the guilt that she felt for her crimes; however, during the cross-examination, the prosecutor succeeded in provoking the defendant until she lost her temper. She stood and screamed in rage.

   "Defense, please _____ your client," said the judge. After the outburst, the trial fell apart for the defense. The jury deliberated and found the defendant guilty, and one of the witnesses faced _____ charges for lying on behalf of the defendant.

From the list below, supply the words needed to complete the paragraph. Some words will not be used.

junta	**sedentary**	**mollify**	**subversive**
patina	**placebo**	**tantamount**	

3. The _____ on the brass buttons of General Blanco's uniform sparkled in the sun when he stepped outside the capital office and fished in his pockets for his pill box. Only his doctor knew that the general was about to take a _____ that consisted of little more than sugar. Days before, the general had demanded treatment for recurring chest pains. The doctor found nothing wrong with the general, so he prescribed a psychological treatment for what he thought was a psychological illness.

   General Blanco's malady was likely the result of a very stressful situation. At the time the pains began, he was a member of a five-person _____ that had seized control of an impoverished nation. Plenty of _____ citizens were more than willing to reinstall the exiled dictator. Blanco had acquired some experience that was _____ to leading a nation, but had little experience in dodging assassins.

Exercise II

Sentence Completion

Complete the sentence in a way that shows you understand the meaning of the italicized vocabulary word.

1. Judging by the *patina* on the doorknob, the house…

2. The *junta* took control of the government after…

3. To some employers, taking office supplies for home use is *tantamount* to…

4. The little girl seemed *plaintive* after…

5. During the *pinnacle* of the story, the heroine…

6. The builder said that warm, damp conditions in the basement are *conducive* to…

7. *Strictures* on the number of fish you can catch are meant to…

8. Pauline's *rigorous* morning workout includes…

9. Ted was fired for *perjury* after he…

10. Some *subversive* citizens refused to acknowledge the new law that…

11. Will attributed his fast recovery to the *influx* of…

12. The photographer required his subjects to be *sedentary* so that…

13. Half the experimental rats received a *placebo*, while the other half received…

14. The usually *amenable* students in the class surprised the substitute teacher by…

15. The police could not *mollify* the man after he learned that…

Exercise III

Roots, Prefixes, and Suffixes

Study the entries and answer the questions that follow.

The root *phon* means "sound."
The prefix *tele–* means "afar" or "at a distance."
The root *put* means "to clean," "to prune," or "to reckon."

1. Using *literal* translations as guidance, define the following words without using a dictionary:

    A. telephone   D. television
    B. repute   E. compute
    C. polyphony   F. symphonic

2. A battlefield surgeon might want to _____ someone's infected limb, but someone who does not think that the operation is necessary might _____ the doctor's decision.

3. List as many words as you can think of that contain the roots *phon* or *put*.

Exercise IV

Inference

Complete the sentence by inferring information about the italicized word from its context.

1. If someone is as *sedentary* as a statue, then that person is...

2. A store might choose an *amenable* person to work in the complaint department because he or she will...

3. If inhalation of asbestos is *conducive* to developing lung cancer, people who work in asbestos mines should...

Exercise V

Writing

Here is a writing prompt similar to the one you will find on the writing portion of an assessment test.

Plan and write an essay based on the following statement:

> There is nothing so horrible as languid study; when you sit looking at the clock, wishing the time was over, or that somebody would call on you and put you out of your misery. The only way to read with any efficacy, is to read so heartily, that dinnertime comes two hours before you expected it.
>
> –Sydney Smith (1771-1845)
> "How to Read"

Assignment: In an essay, explain what Sydney Smith means by "languid study" and discuss the practicality of his suggested remedy for the condition. Support your position with evidence from your reading, classroom studies, experience, and observation.

Thesis: Write a *one-sentence* response to the assignment. Make certain this single sentence offers a clear statement of your position.

Example: Sydney Smith properly advises readers to become entirely absorbed by the material because this focus will make the reading a much more enjoyable experience.

_____

_____

Organizational Plan: List at least three subtopics you will use to support your main idea. This list is your outline.

1. _____

2. _____

3. _____

Draft: Following your outline, write a good first draft of your essay. Remember to support all your points with examples, facts, references to reading, etc.

Review and Revise: Exchange essays with a classmate. Using the Holistic scoring guide on page 256, score your partner's essay (while he or she scores yours). If necessary, rewrite your essay to correct the problems noted by your partner.

Exercise VI

Improving Paragraphs

Read the following passage and then answer the multiple-choice questions that follow. The questions will require you to make decisions regarding the revision of the reading selection.

1   (1) Clothes hangers are one of mankind's greatest peeves because they are a necessary evil. (2) The way in which the simple creatures complicate daily life reveals their satanic inclination. (3) Wire hangers are the worst; it is rumored that they exist solely to irritate the user. (4) At night, while humans sleep, **subversive** wire hangers converse about how they can collectively infuriate people who try to remove hangers from their natural state—the puzzle-like entanglement. (5) Inseparable, the hangers devise ways to best fuse themselves to one another by interweaving their long, thin arms and necks.

2   (6) Sadly, humans appear to be years away from solving the coat hanger dilemma. (7) Even in this age of space exploration, digital information, and quantum physics, we can find no better way to hang clothing than with hangers. (8) We try hooks, which work fairly well, but they leave permanent divots in garments in the spot on which the garment was hanged. (9) A garment hanged by the sleeve, for example, looks rather strange when worn with a pointy bulge emanating from the shoulder.

3   (10) Wood hangers only prove to be greater foes than their wire cousins. (11) They are weighty and bulky, and when they're not used to hang heavy overcoats, they usurp all available space in the closet. (12) When wood hangers are not taking up precious space, they are trying to escape; their most common method is to grab any adjacent wire hanger as it is picked from the rack. (13) Plastic hangers, while mildly more **amenable** than wooden hangers, have their own annoying idiosyncrasies, the first being the tiny hook-like appendages that are allegedly for securing the hanging loops of skirts. (14) These little hooks were obviously engineered by clothing manufacturers because they invariably break off and leave sharp edges to fray the inside of the blouse that accompanies the skirt. (15) It's cruel, indeed, but to make things worse, skirts actually hung by their loops develop distinct creases that make re-ironing necessary. (16) Re-ironing is the ultimate goal of any hanger separated from its nest.

4   (17) One particularly devilish species of hanger is the one with the white cardboard roll on the bottom for hanging slacks without producing a fold mark. (18) These hangers, while not quite as cunning as plastic hangers, are perhaps the most treacherous because they don't even try to function as they are designed. (19) Immediately after placing a load upon the hanger, however minuscule, the cardboard tube collapses into its natural equilibrium—the classic V-shape. (20) The more astute cardboard-roll hangers wait until they have been placed in the closet, out of view, before they collapse. (21) This ensures that they carry out that prime directive of all hangers—to render the clothing wrinkled and unfit for wearing in public.

5   (22) No one knows what the future holds for the human hanger dilemma, but certainly scientists are working around the clock to remedy the blight. (23) Until that solution arrives, we must stay one step ahead of the hangers. (24) We must retaliate and deny their happiness. (25) Ridicule the hanger, and then show it that you're in charge by simply throwing the clothes on the floor and wrinkling them yourself. (26) The next time that you are about to detangle a hanger, stop.

1. Which of the following suggestions would improve the introduction of the passage?
   A. Start paragraph 1 with sentence 4.
   B. Start a new paragraph with sentence 5.
   C. Start paragraph 1 with sentence 6.
   D. Start a new paragraph after sentence 2.
   E. Start a new paragraph after sentence 3.

2. Which of the following corrects a usage error in paragraph 2?
   A. Hyphenate *quantum physics*.
   B. Change *hanged* to *hung*.
   C. Capitalize *age*.
   D. Correct the spelling of *garment*.
   E. Insert a semicolon after *physics*.

3. Which change in the paragraph sequence would improve the organization of the passage?
   A. Exchange paragraph 1 with paragraph 3.
   B. Exchange paragraph 2 with paragraph 3.
   C. Move paragraph 2 so it follows paragraph 4.
   D. Delete paragraph 2.
   E. Delete paragraph 3.

4. Which of the following would best improve paragraph 3?
   A. Begin a new paragraph after sentence 10.
   B. Begin a new paragraph after sentence 11.
   C. Begin a new paragraph after sentence 12.
   D. Begin a new paragraph after sentence 13.
   E. Begin a new paragraph after sentence 14.

5. Which of the following best clarifies paragraph 5?
   A. Exchange sentence 22 with sentence 23.
   B. Exchange sentence 25 with sentence 26.
   C. Exchange sentence 24 with sentence 25.
   D. Delete sentence 26.
   E. Make two sentences from sentence 22.

Lesson Twenty

1. **impasse** (im′ pâs) *n.* a problem or predicament with no obvious resolution
    Fighting resumed when the two factions reached an *impasse* during the peace talks.
    syn: gridlock; stalemate; standoff

2. **crony** (krō′ nē) *n.* a close friend
    Carl and his *cronies* can be found at the bowling alley every Wednesday night.
    syn: buddy; chum   *ant: enemy*

3. **acumen** (ə kyü′ mən, a′ kyə) *n.* ability to discern or discriminate; shrewdness
    Hal's business *acumen* made him an excellent stockbroker.
    syn: keenness; sharpness   *ant: ignorance; naiveté*

4. **nanotechnology** (na nō tek nä′ lə jē) *n.* the use of single atoms and
        molecules to construct microscopic devices
    Scientists hope to use *nanotechnology* to create tiny robots that can be injected into
    the body to destroy cancer cells.

5. **notarize** (nō′ tə rīz) *v.* to certify legally
    Someone will *notarize* the signatures on the title to complete the sale of the car.

6. **insular** (in′ sə ler) *adj.* isolated in thought, as though living on an island
    Joe's *insular* childhood in a remote mountain village left him unaware of just how
    very different people could be.
    syn: provincial; narrow   *ant: worldly; cosmopolitan*

7. **malodorous** (mal ō′ də rəs) *adj.* having an offensive odor
    People ten miles away could smell the *malodorous* chicken processing plant.
    syn: stinking

8. **pungent** (pun′ jənt) *adj.* having a sharp taste; acrid
    The dairy store offered samples of both mild and *pungent* types of cheeses.
    syn: sharp   *ant: mild*

9. **erroneous** (i rō′ nē əs) *adj.* incorrect; mistaken
    Read the questions carefully, or you'll have *erroneous* answers on the test.
    syn: flawed   *ant: correct*

10. **concurrent** (kən kər´ ənt) *adj.* happening at the same time
    This year, Jane's birthday happens to be *concurrent* with Easter.
    syn: simultaneous   *ant: conflicting; separate*

11. **negligible** (ne´ gli jə bəl) *adj.* of little importance; insignificant
    The car was in great shape except for a few *negligible* scratches.
    syn: unimportant; trifling   *ant: significant; noteworthy*

12. **renege** (ri nig´) *v.* to break a promise or obligation; to revoke
    Pete *reneged* on his promise to care for his dog, so his parents gave the animal away.
    syn: breach; default

13. **precept** (prē´ sept) *n.* a rule of action; a principle to live by
    Kim lived by the *precepts* of modesty, courtesy, and moderation.
    syn: law; axiom

14. **visage** (viz´ ij) *n.* a face; a facial expression
    Ken's *visage* turned to anger when he saw the neighbor's dog in his own swimming pool.
    syn: countenance; features

15. **irrevocable** (i re´ və kə bəl) *adj.* impossible to retract or revoke; irreversible
    The decision to divorce was *irrevocable*.
    syn: permanent; unchangeable

Exercise I

Words in Context

From the list below, supply the words needed to complete the paragraph. Some words will not be used.

renege	precept	pungent	notarize
negligible	acumen	visage	erroneous

1. Dave could not help noticing Daria's furious _____ as she pulled her sputtering car into his driveway. She parked the car and stomped across the lawn until she found Dave sitting on the porch.
    "I want my money back," said Daria. "I've had the car for only an hour, so it shouldn't be a problem for you to return the money. This whole episode has left a[n] _____, ugly taste in my mouth."
    "I'm afraid that your assumption is _____," said Dave in a smug tone. "The clerk _____ the sales contract; you bought the car 'as-is,' and the transaction is official. You can't _____ on the deal at this point. Besides, it's not my fault that you didn't have the _____ to realize that the car has flaws." Daria clenched her fists, grumbled, and stormed back to the lemon that she had just purchased.

From the list below, supply the words needed to complete the paragraph. Some words will not be used.

precept	pungent	crony	nanotechnology
irrevocable	impasse	concurrent	

2. "Every word is recorded in this laboratory, so use caution, because anything you say will be _____," Dr. Bryant warned Matt as they walked past the _____ department of the robotics research division. Matt was still ecstatic about his new job with Neutrodyne, a world leader in robotic technology. He took the job because he was afraid that he might reach a[n] _____ working for the government if his political views did not support the nature of his assigned research. He wanted the ability to merge his _____ with his career, and Neutrodyne seemed to be the best place to do it. The fact that a few of his college _____ worked there made the decision quite simple.

From the list below, supply the words needed to complete the paragraph. Some words will not be used.

malodorous	negligible	impasse	insular
concurrent	acumen		

3. Since the Soup Olympics and the Champion Cookoff were _____ this year, Kevin had to make two separate batches of his famous seafood bisque. He stayed up all night before the contests, stirring and seasoning until he felt that the soup was perfect. To an inexperienced taster, Kevin's tiny additions produced _____ changes in the food, but to the judges, Kevin knew, the tiny differences would determine who won and who lost. If the bisque lacked in one particular spice, or if the judge detected the faintest _____ scent from the sample, Kevin would not win first prize. Even second place would make Kevin proud; he had become a master at preparing seafood in spite of his _____ mid-western roots, where meat and potatoes graced virtually every dish, and fish was practically non-existent.

Exercise II

Sentence Completion

Complete the sentence in a way that shows you understand the meaning of the italicized vocabulary word.

1. If Dianne had known that her decision was going to be *irrevocable*, she…

2. Since the flood was *concurrent* with the earthquake, the damage…

3. If no one *notarizes* the contract, it will…

4. After fleeing the police, the mugger found himself at an *impasse* when he…

5. Norman's youthful *visage* disappeared after…

6. The back parking lot was *malodorous* in the summer because…

7. Once a year, Meg calls all her *cronies* together in order to…

8. Brad's parents were confident that their son had the *precepts* to…

9. To give the bread a *pungent* flavor, the cook…

10. The expert in *nanotechnology* lectured the students on…

11. Paul *reneged* on his dinner plans when he found out…

12. One *erroneous* entry in the database will cause…

13. When the *insular* tribe made first contact with the outside world, the biggest shock for them was…

14. The damage to the family car was *negligible*, so Rhonda's parents…

15. Teri's *acumen* in identifying personality types made her good at…

Exercise III

Roots, Prefixes, and Suffixes

Study the entries and answer the questions that follow.

The prefixes *ambi–* and *amphi–* mean "both" or "around."
The roots *luc* and *lum* mean "light."
The prefix *super–* means "above" or "over."
The root *magn* means "great."

1. Using *literal* translations as guidance, define the following words without using a dictionary:

   A. luminary   D. magnitude
   B. translucent   E. magnate
   C. amphibious   F. superintendent

2. Someone who can use both hands equally well is called _____. An *ambiguous* statement can be interpreted in _____.

3. You might use a lamp to _____ your desktop so that you can see your work. If the filament in the light bulb does not become _____, you will know that the bulb is burned out.

4. List as many words as you can think of that contain the root *magn* or the prefix *super–*.

Exercise IV

Inference

Complete the sentence by inferring information about the italicized word from its context.

1. If you *renege* on a deal once, few people will…

2. Sports stars and team owners might reach an *impasse* about contracts if…

3. One good *precept* to remember throughout your life is…

Exercise V

Critical Reading

Below is a pair of reading passages followed by several multiple-choice questions. Carefully read the passages and choose the best answer for each of the questions.

The authors of the following passages focus on Halloween. Both of the passages contain information about the origins of Halloween, but they situate the event in different historical periods.

Passage 1

Lots of people celebrate Halloween, but only a few realize that the origins of the autumn celebration rest in ancient history. The predominant theory about the origins of Halloween is that the celebration descended from the ancient Celtic festival of Samhain.

5   For the Celts living in Ireland and northern England during the fifth century B.C., Samhain was the most important festival of the year. Celebrated on the first of November, Samhain honored the end of the year and marked the beginning of the new year. For the Celts, November was a logical time to observe the new year; November marked the end of the harvest season, which is **concurrent** with winter, a potentially deadly season for early cultures. It was only appropriate that the unstoppable winter, whose biting cold and long dark nights drained the
10   life from both crops and people, was a symbol of death. On the eve of the Celtic New Year— the night that we now call Halloween—the Celts believed that a doorway to the spirit world opened, and that the spirits of those who died throughout the year were free once again to roam the world of the living. During the eve of the new year, the Celts wore costumes, while priests conducted rituals around sacrificial pyres.
15   The beliefs and traditions associated with Samhain slowly changed in the centuries following the peak of Celtic civilization. Romans conquered most of the Celtic lands and had incorporated some of their own beliefs into the Samhain festivities by A.D. 100. After Christianity had spread to Celtic lands by the eighth century, the day of the Celtic New Year became All Hallows, a day of honoring Christian saints. We now refer to the eve of November first as All
20   Hallows' Eve, or Halloween; despite cultural shifts, however, the descendents of the Celts never quite abandoned the ancient belief that spirits roamed the earth on Halloween, often sporting ghostly or grotesque **visages**. People augmented the old Celtic beliefs with new legends, the most notable of which was perhaps the legend that spirits not only roamed the earth, but that they also sought new bodies to possess.
25   Wary of spirit possession, the Celtic descendents had to develop adequate defenses, the first of which was disguise. Having assumed that spirits would ignore their own kind, people disguised themselves as spirits if they ventured outdoors on Halloween. As a second precaution, people placed offerings of food on their doorsteps; they hoped that any evil spirits roaming the night would be satisfied with the food and decline to enter the homes. People who
30   left no treat for the spirits, of course, risked provoking the wandering spirits and rendering themselves prone to tricks.
   Few of the modern Halloween revelers stop to think about the historic roots of the holiday. Many people make the **erroneous** assumption that the holiday symbolizes an assemblage of evil rituals or devil worship, but that is certainly not the case. While the Celts did believe that
35   spirits roamed the earth on the eve of the new year, the traditions that they established were innocent and festive, just as Halloween is today.

Passage 2

Few holidays spark the interests and imaginations of children as well as Halloween does. For nearly a century, Americans have embraced the tradition of decorating homes with the fruits of harvest and donning costumes in an effort to ward off evil spirits and, maybe, scare a few treats out of neighbors.

5   The Halloween that we know did not come into practice until the late nineteenth century. Long dormant in America, the celebration experienced resurgence when the **influx** of Irish and Scottish immigrants brought old Celtic traditions to North America. Americans began dressing up in costumes and, in merriment, went from house to house asking for food. People who offered no food were prone to tricks—good-humored "punishments" for their lack of
10   hospitality.

As poverty increased around the beginning of the twentieth century, young urbanites began to taint the benevolent spirit of Halloween. What were once benign tricks with **negligible** effects slowly became acts of vandalism that only detracted from the autumn festivities. Fearing that such behavior might destroy an enjoyable tradition, people planned ways to turn
15   Halloween into a community event.

Shortly after the turn of the century, communities organized block parties, dances, and other Halloween festivities that brought people together and, at the same time, discouraged the destructive activities of wayward pranksters. People were encouraged to offer small treats as a way to rekindle the festive nature of Halloween and to curb vandalism. This was the birth of
20   the still-popular American Halloween tradition.

While a very small minority claims that Halloween is a time to celebrate the wicked, Halloween, for the majority, is a time of innocent festivity, when families can spend time together and children can explore the limits of their creativity. Controversy will always surround the jovial season and the way in which it is celebrated, but Halloween will always be
25   a source of fun childhood memories and a way to celebrate, or even parody, our fears of the unknown.

1A. The original Celts, according to passage 1, observed Samhain around which of the following time periods?
    A.   1945-1941 B.C.
    B.   500-400 B.C.
    C.   A.D. 100-200
    D.   A.D. 700-800
    E.   The Celts still observe Samhain.

1B. Which time of year was Samhain observed?
    A.   the end of autumn
    B.   the longest day of the year
    C.   the first day of spring
    D.   before the harvest
    E.   the second full moon of October

2A. According to the first passage, the ancient Celts celebrated Samhain for the same reason that modern people might celebrate
    A.   Presidents' Day.
    B.   Boxing Day.
    C.   Halloween.
    D.   New Year.
    E.   Valentine's Day.

2B. Which line from passage 1 best supports your answer to question 2A?
  A. Spirits roamed the earth on Halloween.
  B. November marked the end of the harvest season.
  C. Romans conquered most of the Celtic lands.
  D. November was a logical time to observe the new year.
  E. Samhain honored the end of the year.

3A. According to the first passage, winter was an appropriate symbol of death because
  A. it killed food supplies.
  B. it caused people to freeze.
  C. it caused the death of animals.
  D. it caused the death of plants and people.
  E. it slowed the movement of the spirits.

3B. By the same rationale as exhibited in question 3A, summer would be an appropriate symbol for
  A. the living.
  B. harvesting crops.
  C. water.
  D. the spirit world.
  E. the dying.

4A. Descendants of the Celts thought that disguises would protect them from spirits because
  A. the ancient Celts wore costumes and lived through Halloween.
  B. they thought that spirits would not bother other spirits.
  C. they thought that the spirits would not be able to find them.
  D. they thought spirits could not stand the way that Celts looked.
  E. they thought wearing disguises was a part of the New Year tradition.

4B. If unprepared for supernatural aspects of Samhain, the Celts believed themselves to be in danger of
  A. becoming trapped.
  B. crop shortages.
  C. Viking attacks.
  D. food poisoning.
  E. possession.

5A. In line 22 of the first passage, the word *augmented* most nearly means
  A. supplemented.
  B. rewrote.
  C. abolished.
  D. imitated.
  E. believed.

5B. If the original Celts had *augmented* their food supply, then they would have
    A.   starved.
    B.   changed their religious beliefs.
    C.   had more to eat.
    D.   reduced their consumption.
    E.   changed what they ate.

6A. The intention of the first passage is to
    A.   persuade that Halloween is not evil.
    B.   inform how Halloween influenced the rituals of Samhain.
    C.   develop an argument against Halloween.
    D.   inform about the early roots of Halloween traditions.
    E.   instruct how to emulate the ancient Celts.

6B. Which title below fails to describe the main idea of any of the paragraphs in passage 1?
    A.   Samhain Slowly Changes
    B.   A Fun Tradition
    C.   The Celts and Samhain
    D.   A Holiday of Evil
    E.   Protection on Halloween

7A. According to the second passage, which best describes why Halloween was threatened during the turn of the century?
    A.   Poverty increased.
    B.   Celtic people abandoned their traditions.
    C.   Block parties were not yet popular.
    D.   Children had discipline problems.
    E.   Vandalism increased during Halloween.

7B. Which choice, from passage 2, describes the solution employed to maintain the Halloween tradition?
    A.   extra police patrols
    B.   cheaper treats
    C.   Celtic history studies
    D.   heavy fines for vandalism
    E.   involve more people

8A. As used in line 12 of the second passage, *benign* most nearly means
    A.   harmless.
    B.   expensive.
    C.   legendary.
    D.   illogical.
    E.   careless.

8B. Which line from passage 2 best supports your answer to question 8A?
   A.   "People were encouraged to offer small treats…"
   B.   "…discouraged the destructive activities of wayward pranksters."
   C.   "People who offered no food were prone to tricks—good-humored, 'punishments' for their lack of hospitality."
   D.   "Long dormant in America, the celebration experienced resurgence…"
   E.   "Fearing that such behavior might destroy an enjoyable tradition, people planned ways to turn Halloween into a community event."

9A. The authors of both passages would probably agree that
   A.   Halloween is detrimental to children.
   B.   Halloween should be practiced like Samhain.
   C.   Halloween is an inoffensive, festive celebration.
   D.   Samhain should be illegal.
   E.   Modern practices are nearly perfect imitations of the ancient Celtic rituals.

9B. In contrast to the answer to question 9A, what did the ancient tradition of Samhain include that might be considered negative?
   A.   farming
   B.   sacrificial fires
   C.   robes
   D.   cold winters
   E.   spirit possession

10A. The two passages differ most in
   A.   tone—the first is argumentative, while the second is strictly informative.
   B.   topic—the first informs about ancient history, while the second informs about modern history.
   C.   subject—the first informs about Celts, while the second informs about Halloween.
   D.   setting—they take place in different areas of the world.
   E.   characters—the Romans are not mentioned in the second passage.

10B. The title that would best suit either of the passages is
   A.   America's Favorite Holiday.
   B.   Ancient Halloween.
   C.   Modern Halloween.
   D.   The History of Halloween.
   E.   The Many Aspects of Halloween.

Lesson Twenty-One

1. **confute** (kən fyōōt´) *v.* to argue or point out an error
The candidate *confuted* every aspect of his opponent's proposed policies.
syn: refute; disprove   *ant: confirm; verify*

2. **meritorious** (mer ə tôr´ ē əs) *adj.* deserving of an award or honor
The young corporal won a medal for his *meritorious* actions in combat.
syn: commendable; laudable; praiseworthy   *ant: despicable; unworthy*

3. **mezzanine** (mez ə nēn´) *n.* the lowest balcony in a theater; a partial story
between main stories in a building
Kelly had an excellent view of the show from her seat in the *mezzanine*.

4. **tribulation** (tri byə lā´ shən) *n.* an affliction, trouble, or difficult experience
The death of Betty's father was a time of *tribulation* for the entire family.
syn: ordeal; hardship

5. **recumbent** (ri kəm´ bənt) *adj.* resting or lying down
The *recumbent* children soon fell asleep.
syn: reclining   *ant: upright*

6. **dynasty** (dī´ nəs tē) *n.* a succession of rulers from the same family or group
The Romanov *dynasty* ruled Russia for more than 300 years.

7. **purport** (pər pôrt´) *v.* to claim; to give a false impression
The newspaper *purports* to be objective, but it is actually very biased in its reporting.
syn: allege; claim; maintain

8. **forte** (fôrt, fôr tā´) *n.* an area of expertise or strength
Jane is good at mathematics, but science is her *forte*.
syn: specialty; talent   *ant: weakness*

9. **kleptomania** (klep tə mān´ ē ə) *n.* a continual urge to steal regardless of
economic motive
Unable to control her *kleptomania*, the wealthy actress shoplifted a pair of shoes.

10. **renown** (ri noun´) *n.* the state of being well known and honored; fame
The actor enjoyed world *renown* after starring in a blockbuster film.
syn: notoriety; popularity   *ant: anonymity; obscurity*

11. **ineffable**   (i ne´ fə bəl)   *adj.*   too sacred or great to be described; indescribable
Lynn could not believe the *ineffable* beauty of the mountains in the distance.
syn: inexpressible

12. **fortitude**   (for´ tə tōōd)   *n.*   strength in adversity
If not for the *fortitude* of the soldiers on the front line, we would have lost the battle.
syn: determination; tenacity   *ant: weakness*

13. **botch**   (bätch)   *v.*   to ruin through clumsiness; to bungle
Bill *botched* the experiment when he forgot to water the plants.
syn: err   *ant: fix*

14. **perennial**   (pə ren´ ē əl)   *adj.*   lasting indefinitely
The parents tried to instill a *perennial* feeling of worth in their child.
syn: enduring; perpetual   *ant: fleeting; limited*

15. **brinkmanship**   (brink´ mən ship)   *n.*   pushing dangerous situations to the edge
of disaster rather than conceding
President Kennedy's blockade during the Cuban Missile Crisis could have led to
nuclear war, but this act of *brinkmanship* ended with the peaceful removal
of weapons.

Exercise I

Words in Context

From the list below, supply the words needed to complete the paragraph. Some words will not be used.

renown	**forte**	**confute**	**brinkmanship**
dynasty	**recumbent**	**tribulation**	

1. Damian mounted his new _____ bicycle, but he immediately crashed into a light pole because he was not used to sitting back while riding a bike. After a few minutes of _____, though, he was able to ride around in the parking lot without falling down. Damian's friends _____ his decision to spend a lot of money on what they called a novelty item, but Damian was _____ for wasting money on things that sat in the basement and collected dust when he tired of them. His credit card sprees would stop eventually. Damian was bound to lose his game of financial _____, in which he waited to pay his bills until he received threatening notices from the bank.

From the list below, supply the words needed to complete the paragraph. Some words will not be used.

fortitude	**perennial**	**recumbent**	**meritorious**
forte	**botch**	**purport**	

2. Mohandas Gandhi never _____ to be a great leader, and his _____ was certainly not his public speaking ability. Nonetheless, Gandhi's _____ service to his people brought independence to India, and his _____ message, that any nation willing to unite in patience and _____ can overcome its oppressors, will be remembered forever.

From the list below, supply the words needed to complete the paragraph. Some words will not be used.

mezzanine	**dynasty**	**tribulation**	**kleptomania**
botch	**ineffable**	**meritorious**	

3. During preparation for his twenty-first burglary, Simon wondered if, perhaps, he suffered from a type of _____. He had already amassed a small fortune from the sale of stolen art, but he always seemed to need to pull off "just one more job" before he retired permanently. He almost retired involuntarily when he _____ the last job by dropping a statuette of _____ beauty from the _____ of the art museum while fumbling with his night-vision goggles. The relic, which dated back to the Ming _____, shattered when it struck the floor far below.

Exercise II

Sentence Completion

Complete the sentence in a way that shows you understand the meaning of the italicized vocabulary word.

1. Jake planned to spend his afternoon *recumbent* in…

2. Judy longed for the life of *renown* that only…

3. I *confuted* the question on the test because it…

4. From the *mezzanine* in the factory, the foreman shouted…

5. If math is not your *forte*, then you should…

6. Davy *botched* the car's paint job when he…

7. The hostage crisis turned into a dangerous game of *brinkmanship* when the criminal threatened to…

8. The school honored Nicole's *meritorious* academic achievements by…

9. It is important for citizens to maintain their *fortitude* during…

10. Unless you have some form of *kleptomania*, there's no reason for you…

11. In a few minutes, the *tribulation* of learning how to swim was over and Clarence was able to…

12. For two hundred years, the *dynasty*…

13. The man *purports* to be an expert, but really he…

14. The *ineffable* sight of Earth from the spacecraft caused…

15. April hoped to find *perennial* happiness by…

Exercise III

Roots, Prefixes, and Suffixes

Study the entries and answer the questions that follow.

The roots *doc* and *doct* mean "to teach" or "to cause."
The roots *au* and *esthe* mean "to feel," "to perceive," or "to hear."
The roots *cad* and *cas* mean "to fall" or "to die."

1. Using *literal* translations as guidance, define the following words without using a dictionary:

    A. document   D. audition
    B. auditorium   E. anesthetize
    C. cadence   F. aesthetic

2. The word _____ literally translates to "teacher," and a _____ student is easy to teach.

3. A _____ is a dead or fallen soldier, and medical students practice their surgical techniques on *cadavers*, which are _____.

4. List as many words as you can think of that contain the root *au*.

Exercise IV

Inference

Complete the sentence by inferring information about the italicized word from its context.

1. If you continue to *confute* the boss in front of the other workers, you might…

2. For her *meritorious* actions that saved two lives, the lifeguard was…

3. Because he was *recumbent* in his hammock, Pete did not…

Exercise V

Writing

Here is a writing prompt similar to the one you will find on the writing portion of an assessment test.

Plan and write an essay based on the following statement:

> It irritates me to be told how things have always been done…I defy
> the tyranny of precedent.
>
> —Clara Barton (1821-1912)

Assignment: Write an essay in which you explain what Clara Barton meant by the phrase, "tyranny of precedent." Support or refute her view. Support your argument with evidence from your reading, classroom studies, experience, and observation.

Thesis: Write a *one-sentence* response to the assignment. Make certain this single sentence offers a clear statement of your position.

> *Example: Clara Barton's advocacy of defying precedents, or established values, is not always an effective course of action.*

_____

_____

Organizational Plan: List at least three subtopics you will use to support your main idea. This list is your outline.

1. _____

2. _____

3. _____

Draft: Following your outline, write a good first draft of your essay. Remember to support all your points with examples, facts, references to reading, etc.

Review and Revise: Exchange essays with a classmate. Using the Holistic scoring guide on page 256, score your partner's essay (while he or she scores yours). If necessary, rewrite your essay to correct the problems noted by your partner.

Exercise VI

English Practice

Identifying Sentence Errors

Identify the grammatical error in each of the following sentences. If the sentence contains no error, select answer choice E.

1. When people buy cell phones, you should be able to afford the
   (A)   (B)   (C)
   roaming charges.   No error
   (D)   (E)

2. The psychiatrist found Marguerite to have no self-confidence in herself
                          (A)   (B)   (C)
   whatsoever.   No error
   (D)   (E)

3. We thought it was bazaar to see Marvin wear his toupee backwards, but he
              (A)   (B)   (C)
   seemed to think it was cute.   No error
        (D)   (E)

4. The next time that you go to the office store, I would like you to get me these
                    (A)   (B)   (C)
   kind of pens.   No error
   (D)   (E)

5. If Bob had begun the inspection earlier, he would have completed the required
            (A)   (B)   (C)
   repairs before the general's visit.   No error
                      (D)   (E)

Improving Sentences

The underlined portion of each sentence below contains some flaw. Select the answer choice that best corrects the flaw.

6. His new pinstriped suit was worn by him to the last dance of the school year.
   A. He wore a new pinstriped suit
   B. His pinstriped suit, new, was worn
   C. He wore his new pinstriped suit
   D. The worn pinstriped suit he wore
   E. The new pinstriped suit was worn by him

7. Pat based the decision for his testimony on the old proverb that <u>honesty was the best policy.</u>
    A. honesty is the best policy.
    B. "honesty was the best policy".
    C. honesty, was the best policy.
    D. "honesty is not always the best policy."
    E. honesty was a good policy.

8. Teachers have shown that children have a keener aptitude <u>for learning than an adult.</u>
    A. for learning than an adult has.
    B. for adult-level learning.
    C. than an adult has for learning.
    D. for learning than an adult's aptitude.
    E. for learning than adults have.

9. <u>We had an upright piano built for a student with a transparent front.</u>
    A. We had an upright piano built with a transparent front for a student.
    B. We had an upright piano with a transparent front built for a student.
    C. We had a student upright piano with a transparent front built.
    D. An upright piano built for a student had a transparent front and we had it.
    E. We had a transparent front upright piano that was built for a student.

10. <u>Don't expect Harold, Mimi, and I</u> to arrive promptly at an early morning meeting.
    A. Don't expect Harold, Mimi, and me
    B. Harold, Mimi, and me should not be expected
    C. Don't expect a meeting with Harold, Mimi, and I
    D. Harold, Mimi and I cannot be expected
    E. Don't expect Mimi, I, and Harold

Review Lessons 19-21

Exercise I

Inferences

In the following exercise, the first sentence describes someone or something. Infer information from the first sentence, and then choose the word from the Word Bank that best completes the second sentence.

brinkmanship	perennial	irrevocable	concurrent
stricture	plaintive	amenable	renege

1. The school was quiet in the hours following the tornado, except for the soft whimpering of a trapped dog.

    From this sentence, we can infer that the dog was making _____ sounds.

2. Colin agreed to sell his dirt bike, but then refused to accept the money and took the bike home instead.

    From this sentence, we can infer that Colin _____ on his deal to sell the dirt bike.

3. For a few months, the ruler of the poverty-stricken nation threatened to increase nuclear weapons testing unless other nations provided more food; however, his threats ceased when the other nations began preparing for war instead of sending supplies.

    From this sentence, we can infer that the ruler used _____ to extort food from other nations.

4. The senator hoped that he would have enough votes to pass the bill he proposed.

    From this sentence, we can infer that several other senators must be _____ to the proposal for it to succeed.

5. No matter how many times Tim tried to get his dad to buy a new car, the old man refused.

    From this sentence, we can infer that the father's decision was _____.

Exercise II

Related Words

Some of the vocabulary words from Lessons 19 through 21 have related meanings. Complete the following sentences by choosing the word that best fits the context, based on information you infer from the use of the italicized word. Some word pairs will be antonyms, some will be synonyms, and some will simply be words often used in the same context.

1. A shattered vertebrae forced Dan to stay in a *recumbent* position for months, and it took him a long time to adjust to the _____ lifestyle.
    A. sedentary
    B. subversive
    C. conducive
    D. perennial
    E. erroneous

2. As far as the Protites were concerned, the Venisian commander's *irrevocable* insult was _____ to a declaration of intergalactic war, whether or not he specifically said as much.
    A. tantamount
    B. pungent
    C. catholic
    D. ineffable
    E. rigorous

3. Smoking, drinking, and eating a diet high in simple sugars is not _____ to anyone's *perennial* health, no matter how great his or her genetics might be.
    A. concurrent
    B. recumbent
    C. subversive
    D. renown
    E. conducive

4. Netty *confuted* Bill's calculations, showing him how a[n] _____ factor caused the whole equation to be incorrect.
    A. negligible
    B. erroneous
    C. impermeable
    D. perennial
    E. tantamount

5. Molly _____ on her promise to purchase the grand piano, and she attempted to *mollify* the disappointed salesman by buying a few piano lesson books.
    A. desisted
    B. reneged
    C. botched
    D. renowned
    E. notarized

6. Knowing that his days were numbered, grandpa tried to impart the *acumen* his children would need to survive the _____ they were sure to endure following the declaration of civil war.
   A. tribulations
   B. mezzanines
   C. patina
   D. precepts
   E. influx

7. The judge warned the witness that if she _____ that the suspect is guilty, but she hadn't actually witnessed the crime, then she would be guilty of *perjury*.
   A. garbles
   B. notarizes
   C. cavorts
   D. reneges
   E. purports

8. The *junta* stormed the capital palace, captured the family members of the ruling _____, and mercifully sent them all into exile, ending the family's 113-year reign.
   A. sedentary
   B. dynasty
   C. precept
   D. tribulation
   E. mezzanine

9. When the factions reached an *impasse* over who would control the seaport, the two sides escalated threats toward each other, with each side hoping the other would be the first to cave under the stress of the continued _____.
   A. nanotechnology
   B. decadence
   C. brinkmanship
   D. placebo
   E. kleptomania

10. The defense lawyer argued that his client suffered legitimate *kleptomania* and had not stolen the town's traffic light just to entertain _____ tendencies.
    A. insular
    B. aloof
    C. ineffable
    D. subversive
    E. perennial

Exercise III

Deeper Meanings

Choose a word to replace the italicized word in each sentence. All of the possible choices for each sentence have similar definitions, but the correct answer will have a connotation that best suits the context. For example, the words "delete," "destroy," and "obliterate" all mean "to remove or wipe out," but no one would ever say, "I destroyed the name from the document." The correct choice will be the word that has the best specific meaning and does not render the sentence awkward in tone or content. When choices seem close, look for a clue in the context that makes one choice better than the other.

Note that the correct answer is not always the primary vocabulary word from the lesson.

goofed	sedentary	irrevocable	acumen
visage	unmoving	mug	permanent
lifeless	cunning	botched	

1. As a farmer, Boyd depended on his *skill* to select the seed that would be most productive in the season's expected weather conditions.

   Better word: _____

2. For many years after the terrible inferno, the fireman's dreams were haunted by the panicked *look* of the one victim he was not able to save.

   Better word: _____

3. Mark realized his insult was *final* when his attempts to apologize went unheard, and his friend left the party and never called him again.

   Better word: _____

4. The doctor told Al that he needed to exercise because his *still* office job had left him in terrible health.

   Better word: _____

5. The doctor knew that if she *failed* the surgical procedure, the patient would never recover from his brain injury.

   Better word: _____

Crossword Puzzle

Use the clues to complete the crossword puzzle. The answers consist of vocabulary words from Lessons 19 through 21.

Across

2. pull out of the deal
3. kicking back
5. not worth mentioning
8. the new bosses, by force
11. like a rebel
13. year after year
14. a sugar pill
15. limit
16. new boss, same family
17. really mess up

Down

1. like a couch potato
4. dangerous standoff
6. top of the world
7. guess
9. hard time
10. mistaken
12. rule to live by
13. an old film

Exercise V

Subject Prompts

Here is a writing prompt similar to the one you will find on the writing portion of an assessment test. Follow the instructions below and write a brief, efficient essay.

> As society becomes more averse to violence, and politicians seize upon sensationalized events to use as justification to propose bills that often become laws, some schools have enacted bans on any form of physical contact between students. Some bans disallow far more than the already governed public displays of affection or fighting in the halls; the latest bans restrict everything. A simple tap on the shoulder or a hug to console a friend is now an offense that can blemish a permanent record.
>
> Have schools forgotten the reality of day-to-day human existence? Are they enforcing impossible rules and forgoing discipline in the name of protecting students? Take a side in the argument for or against no-touching policies in schools and write a letter to your school board. Support your position with at least three subtopics based on your own observations and experience.

Thesis: Write a *one-sentence* response to the assignment. Make certain this single sentence offers a clear statement of your position.

Example: Students who lack enough discipline to keep their hands to themselves have no business graduating high school.

_____

_____

Organizational Plan: List at least three subtopics you will use to support your main idea. This list is your outline.

1. _____

2. _____

3. _____

Draft: Following your outline, write a good first draft of your essay. Remember to support all your points with examples, facts, references to reading, etc.

Review and Revise: Exchange essays with a classmate. Using the scoring guide for Development on page 252, score your partner's essay (while he or she scores yours). Focus on the development of ideas and the use of language conventions. If necessary, rewrite your essay to incorporate more (or more relevant) support and/or improve your use of language.

Scoring Guide for Writing

Organization

6 = Clearly Competent

The paper is **clearly** organized **around the central point or main idea**. The organization may grow from the writer's argument or a slightly predictable structure. Ideas follow a logical order.

The work is **free of surface errors** (grammar, spelling, punctuation, etc.).

5 = Reasonably Competent

The organization of the paper is **clear, but not fully implemented**. The structure might be predictable. Ideas follow a logical order, but transitions might be simple or obvious.

Minor surface errors are present, but they **do not interfere** with the reader's understanding of the work.

4 = Adequately Competent

The organization of the paper is **apparent, but not consistently implemented**. The structure is predictable. Some ideas follow a logical order, but transitions are simple and obvious.

Surface errors are present, but they **do not severely interfere** with the reader's understanding.

3 = Nearly Competent

There is **evidence of a** simple organizational **plan**. Ideas are grouped logically in parts of the paper, but do not flow logically throughout. Transitions are needed.

Surface errors are **apparent** and **begin to interfere** with the reader's understanding of the work.

2 = Marginally Incompetent

The organizational plan of the paper is **obscured by too few details** and/or **irrelevant details**. Some of the ideas are grouped logically in parts of the paper. Transitions are needed or are incorrect.

Surface errors are **frequent and severe enough** to **interfere** with the reader's understanding of the work.

1 = Incompetent

There is **no** clear organizational **plan** and/or **insufficient material**. Ideas are not grouped logically. Transitions are absent.

Surface errors are **frequent** and **extreme**, and **severely interfere** with the reader's understanding of the work.

Scoring Guide for Writing

Development

6 = Clearly Competent

The **paper takes a position** on the issue and **offers sufficient material** (details, examples, anecdotes, supporting facts, etc.) to create a **complete discussion. Every word and sentence is relevant**. Ideas are **fully supported**.

The paper visits **different perspectives** of the argument or addresses **counterarguments** to the writer's position. The paper **focuses** on the argument evoked by the prompt. There is a **clear, purposed**, well-developed **introduction** and **conclusion**.

The work is **free of surface errors** (grammar, spelling, punctuation, etc.).

5 = Reasonably Competent

The essay **takes a position** on the issue and **offers sufficient material** for a complete discussion, but the reader is left **with a few unanswered questions**. Ideas are **supported**. The paper **partially visits different perspectives** of the argument or addresses **counterarguments**. **Most of the paper focuses** on the argument evoked by the prompt. There is **no irrelevant material**. There is a clear **introduction** and **conclusion**.

Minor surface errors are present, but they **do not interfere** with the reader's understanding of the work.

4 = Adequately Competent

The paper **takes a position** on the issue but **does not provide** enough details, examples, or supporting facts for a complete discussion, leaving a **few unanswered questions**. The paper includes **some attention** to **counterarguments** and differing perspectives. **Irrelevant material** is present. **Most** of the paper **focuses** on the topic and the specific argument.

Surface errors are present, but they **do not severely interfere** with the reader's understanding.

3 = Nearly Competent

The essay **takes a position** on the issue but **does not include** sufficient details, examples, or supporting facts for a discussion. The paper **may include incomplete or unclear counterarguments**. The paper **might repeat** details or rhetoric. The paper focuses on the topic, but **does not maintain** the specific argument.

Surface errors are **apparent** and **begin to interfere** with the reader's understanding of the work.

2 = Marginally Incompetent

The paper **may not take a position** on the issue, or the paper may take a position but **fail to support** it with sufficient details. Examples and ideas are **vague** and **irrelevant**. The paper might **repeat ideas extensively**. The paper **might maintain focus** on the general topic.

Surface errors are **frequent and severe enough** to **interfere** with the reader's understanding of the work.

1 = Incompetent

The paper **might attempt to take a position**, but it **fails to provide** examples, fact, or rhetoric to support the position. The paper may be **repetitious** with **little** or **no focus** on the general topic.

Surface errors are **frequent** and **extreme**, and **severely interfere** with the reader's understanding of the work.

Scoring Guide for Writing

Sentence Formation And Variety

6 = Clearly Competent
Sentences are **varied, complete**, and **assist the reader** in the flow of
the discussion.
The work is **free of surface errors** (grammar, spelling, punctuation, etc.).

5 = Reasonably Competent
Sentences are **somewhat varied, generally correct**, and **do not distract** the reader
from the flow of the discussion.
Minor surface errors are present, but they **do not interfere** with the reader's
understanding of the work.

4 = Adequately Competent
Some sentences show **variety**, and **most** are **complete** and
generally correct.
Surface errors are present, but they **do not interfere** with the reader's
understanding.

3 = Nearly Competent
Sentences show a **little variety**, but the structure may be **dull**. Sentences are
generally complete and grammatically correct, but **some errors** distract
the reader.
Surface errors are **apparent** and **begin to interfere** with the reader's understanding
of the work.

2 = Marginally Incompetent
Sentence Structure is **usually simple. Problems** in **sentence structure** and
grammar distract the reader and provide **little or no variety**.
Surface errors are **frequent and severe enough to interfere** with the reader's
understanding of the work.

1 = Incompetent
Sentence structure is **simple, generally erroneous** and **lacks variety**.
Surface errors are **frequent** and **extreme**, and **severely interfere** with the reader's
understanding of the work.

Scoring Guide for Writing

Word Choice

6 = Clearly Competent

The essay shows a **good command** of language. Word choice is **specific, clear**, and **vivid**, favoring **powerful nouns** and **verbs** to weaker adjective and adverb phrases. **Clear, specific words** are used, instead of vague, general terms.

The work is **free of surface errors** (grammar, spelling, punctuation, etc.).

5 = Reasonably Competent

Language is **competent**. Word choice is **clear** and **accurate**. Words and phrases are **mostly** vivid, specific, and powerful.

Minor surface errors are present, but they **do not interfere** with the reader's understanding of the work.

4 = Adequately Competent

Language is **adequate**, with **appropriate** word choice. **Most** words and phrases are vivid, specific, and powerful.

Serious surface errors are present, but they **do not interfere** with the reader's understanding.

3 = Nearly Competent

Language shows a **basic control** and word choice is **usually appropriate** but **inconsistent**.

Surface errors are **apparent** and **begin to interfere** with the reader's understanding of the work.

2 = Marginally Incompetent

Word choice is usually **vague**.

Surface errors are **frequent** and **severe enough** to **interfere** with the reader's understanding of the work.

1 = Incompetent

Word choice is **simple, vague**, and **inexact**. The writer makes **no attempt** to choose the best words for the topic, audience, and purpose.

Surface errors are **frequent** and **extreme**, and **severely interfere** with the reader's understanding of the work.

Scoring Guide for Writing

Holistic

6 = Clearly Competent

The paper is **clearly organized** around the central idea. Ideas follow a **logical order**.

The paper **takes a position** on the issue and **offers sufficient material** (details, examples, anecdotes, supporting facts, etc.) to create a complete discussion. There is a **clear, purposed, well-developed** introduction and conclusion.

The paper visits **different perspectives** of the argument or addresses **counterarguments** to the writer's position.

Sentences are **varied, complete,** and **assist the reader** in the flow of the discussion.

The paper shows a **good command** of language. Word choice is **specific, clear,** and **vivid,** favoring **powerful nouns** and **verbs** to weaker adjective and adverb phrases.

The work is **free of surface errors** (grammar, spelling, punctuation, etc.).

5 = Reasonably Competent

The organization of the paper is **clear,** but **not fully implemented**. Ideas follow a **logical order,** but transitions **might be simple** or obvious. The structure **might be predictable**.

The paper **takes a position** on the issue and **offers sufficient material** for a complete discussion, but the reader is left with **a few unanswered questions**. There is a clear **introduction** and **conclusion**.

The paper visits **some different perspectives** of the argument or addresses **counterarguments**.

Sentences are **somewhat varied, generally correct,** and **do not distract** the reader from the flow of the discussion.

Language is **competent**. Words and phrases are **mostly vivid, specific,** and **powerful**.

Minor surface errors are present, but they **do not interfere** with the reader's understanding of the work.

4 = Adequately Competent

The organization of the paper is **apparent**, but **not consistently** implemented. The structure is **predictable**. **Some** ideas follow a **logical order**, but transitions are **simple** and **obvious**. **Most** of the paper **focuses** on the topic and the specific argument.

The paper **takes a position** on the issue, but **does not provide** the details, examples, or supporting facts for a complete discussion, leaving **a few unanswered questions**.

The paper includes **little attention** to counterarguments and differing perspectives.

Irrelevant material is present.

Language is **adequate**, with appropriate word choice. **Most** words and phrases are vivid, specific, and powerful.

Some sentences show **variety**, and **most** are **complete** and **generally correct**.

Surface errors are present, but they **do not interfere** with the reader's understanding.

3 = Nearly Competent

There is **evidence of a simple organizational plan**. The essay **takes a position** on the issue but **does not include** sufficient details, examples, or supporting facts for a discussion. Ideas are **grouped logically** in parts of the paper, **but do not flow** logically throughout. The paper **focuses** on the topic, but **does not maintain** the specific argument.

The paper **may include incomplete** or **unclear** counterarguments.

Language shows a **basic control**, and word choice is **usually appropriate** but **inconsistent**. Sentences show a **little variety**, but the structure may be **dull**.

Sentences are **generally complete** and **grammatically correct**, but some errors **distract** the reader.

The paper might **repeat** details or rhetoric.

Surface errors are **apparent** and **begin to interfere** with the reader's understanding of the work.

2 = Marginally Incompetent

The organizational plan of the paper is **obscured by too few details** and/or **irrelevant details**. The paper **may not take a position** on the issue, or the paper may take a position but **fail to support** it with sufficient details. **Some** of the ideas are **grouped logically** in parts of the paper. The paper **generally maintains focus** on the general topic.

Examples and ideas are **vague** and **irrelevant**.

Sentence structure is **usually simple**. **Problems** in sentence structure and grammar **distract** the reader and provide **little** or **no variety**. **Word choice** is usually **vague**.

The paper might **repeat** ideas **extensively**.

Surface errors are **frequent and severe enough** to **interfere** with the reader's understanding of the work.

1 = Incompetent

There is **no clear organizational plan** and/or **insufficient material**. The paper **might attempt** to **take a position**, but it **fails** to provide examples, fact, or rhetoric to support the position. Ideas are **not grouped logically**.

The paper may be **repetitious** with little or **no focus** on the general topic.

Sentence structure is **simple** and **generally erroneous** and **lacking variety**. Word choice is **simple**, **vague**, and **inexact**. The writer makes **no attempt** to choose the best words for the topic, audience, and purpose.

Surface errors are **frequent** and **extreme**, and **severely interfere** with the reader's understanding of the work.

Relevant State Standards

High School - Grades 9-10

These are only the minimum standards that the product line meets; if these standards seem out of order, they typically go in "keyword" order; from the Language Usage category of standards, to Comprehension, Analysis, Writing, Research/Applied, and Technology/Media categories. Therefore, these standards may be in a different order than the order given by your local Department of Education. Also, if one state standard meets multiple categories, that particular standard is listed the first time it appears, to reduce redundancy. Again, please refer to your local Department of Education for details on the particular standards.

Bias/Validity standards are included, as are Voice/Style standards, as both categories include use of words for different effects on the audience (connotation, denotation, distortion, formality, etc.) and, thus, are logical inclusions.

Depending on the state, standards pertaining to use of dialect and idiomatic expressions might be met by this product. Please refer to your local Department of Education for details.

Notation is as close as possible to the notation given by the Department of Education of the respective state.

States:

Alaska:
R4.1.1-4; R4.4.1-2; R4.5.1; R4.5.2-3; W4 (all); R4.1.5; R4.2.1-2; R4.3.1-4; R4.3.5-6; R4.7.1; R4.9.2; R4.9.1; R4.6.1-4; R4.9.1

Indiana:
10.1.1-4; 10.2.3; 10.3.1; 10.2.1; 10.3.7-8; 10.4 (all); 10.6 (all); 10.5 (all); 10.3.11; 10.7.12; 10.3.12; 10.3.6; 10.3.2; 10.4.10-12

Nebraska (standards set at grade 12):
12.1.1; 12.1.5; 12.1.6

Texas (TEKS section 110.43):
b6 (all); b7 (all); b8B; b11D; b12A; b2 (all); b3 (all); b12B-C; B8D; B9A; B11A, F; B5 (entire)

Virginia:
10.4; 10.3; 10.7; 10.8; 10.3D; 10.9

Common Core State Standards for English Language Arts

Standards	Exercises

Reading Standards for Informational Text

Key Ideas and Details

RI.9-10.1	Cite strong and thorough textual evidence to support analysis of what the text says explicitly as well as inferences drawn from the text.	**Critical Reading** Lessons: 2, 4, 6, 8, 10, 12, 14, 16, 18, 20
RI.9-10.2	Determine a central idea of a text and analyze its development over the course of the text, including how it emerges and is shaped and refined by specific details; provide an objective summary of the text.	**Critical Reading** Lessons: 2, 4, 6, 8, 10, 12, 14, 16, 18, 20

Craft and Structure

RI.9-10.4	Determine the meaning of words and phrases as they are used in a text, including figurative, connotative, and technical meanings; analyze the cumulative impact of specific word choices on meaning and tone (e.g., how the language of a court opinion differs from that of a newspaper).	**Critical Reading** Lessons: 2, 4, 6, 8, 10, 12, 14, 16, 18, 20 **Inference** Lessons: 1-21
RI.9-10.6	Determine an author's point of view or purpose in a text and analyze how an author uses rhetoric to advance that point of view or purpose.	**Critical Reading** Lessons: 2, 4, 6, 8, 10, 12, 14, 16, 18, 20

Writing Standards

Text Types and Purposes

W.9-10.1	Write arguments to support claims in an analysis of substantive topics or texts, using valid reasoning and relevant and sufficient evidence.	**Writing** Lessons: 1, 3, 5, 7, 9, 11, 13, 15, 17, 19, 21
W.9-10.1a	Introduce precise claim(s), distinguish the claim(s) from alternate or opposing claims, and create an organization that establishes clear relationships among claim(s), counterclaims, reasons, and evidence.	**Writing** Lessons: 1, 3, 5, 7, 9, 11, 13, 15, 17, 19, 21
W.9-10.1b	Develop claim(s) and counterclaims fairly, supplying evidence for each while pointing out the strengths and limitations of both in a manner that anticipates the audience's knowledge level and concerns.	**Writing** Lessons: 1, 3, 5, 7, 9, 11, 13, 15, 17, 19, 21
W.9-10.1c	Use words, phrases, and clauses to link the major sections of the text, create cohesion, and clarify the relationships between claim(s) and reasons, between reasons and evidence, and between claim(s) and counterclaims.	**Writing** Lessons: 1, 3, 5, 7, 9, 11, 13, 15, 17, 19, 21

W.9–10.1d	Establish and maintain a formal style and objective tone while attending to the norms and conventions of the discipline in which they are writing.	**Writing** Lessons: 1, 3, 5, 7, 9, 11, 13, 15, 17, 19, 21
W.9–10.1e	Provide a concluding statement or section that follows from and supports the argument presented.	**Writing** Lessons: 1, 3, 5, 7, 9, 11, 13, 15, 17, 19, 21
W.9–10.2	Write informative/explanatory texts to examine and convey complex ideas, concepts, and information clearly and accurately through the effective selection, organization, and analysis of content.	**Writing** Lessons: 1, 3, 5, 7, 9, 11, 13, 15, 17, 19, 21
W.9–10.2a	Introduce a topic; organize complex ideas, concepts, and information to make important connections and distinctions; include formatting (e.g., headings), graphics (e.g., figures, tables), and multimedia when useful to aiding comprehension.	**Writing** Lessons: 1, 3, 5, 7, 9, 11, 13, 15, 17, 19, 21
W.9–10.2b	Develop the topic with well-chosen, relevant, and sufficient facts, extended definitions, concrete details, quotations, or other information and examples appropriate to the audience's knowledge of the topic.	**Writing** Lessons: 1, 3, 5, 7, 9, 11, 13, 15, 17, 19, 21
W.9–10.2c	Use appropriate and varied transitions to link the major sections of the text, create cohesion, and clarify the relationships among complex ideas and concepts.	**Writing** Lessons: 1, 3, 5, 7, 9, 11, 13, 15, 17, 19, 21
W.9–10.2d	Use precise language and domain-specific vocabulary to manage the complexity of the topic.	**Writing** Lessons: 1, 3, 5, 7, 9, 11, 13, 15, 17, 19, 21
W.9–10.2e	Establish and maintain a formal style and objective tone while attending to the norms and conventions of the discipline in which they are writing.	**Writing** Lessons: 1, 3, 5, 7, 9, 11, 13, 15, 17, 19, 21
W.9–10.2f	Provide a concluding statement or section that follows from and supports the information or explanation presented (e.g., articulating implications or the significance of the topic).	**Writing** Lessons: 1, 3, 5, 7, 9, 11, 13, 15, 17, 19, 21

Range of Writing		
W.9-10.10	Write routinely over extended time frames (time for research, reflection, and revision) and shorter time frames (a single sitting or a day or two) for a range of tasks, purposes, and audiences.	**Writing** Lessons: 1, 3, 5, 7, 9, 11, 13, 15, 17, 19, 21

Language Standards

Conventions of Standard English

L.9-10.1a	Demonstrate command of the conventions of standard English grammar and usage when writing or speaking.	**Identifying Sentence Errors** Lessons: 1, 5, 9, 13, 17, 21 **Improving Sentences** Lessons: 1, 5, 9, 13, 17, 21 **Improving Paragraphs** Lessons: 3, 7, 11, 15, 19 **Writing** Lessons: 1, 3, 5, 7, 9, 11, 13, 15, 17, 19, 21
L.9-10.2	Demonstrate command of the conventions of standard English capitalization, punctuation, and spelling when writing.	**Identifying Sentence Errors** Lessons: 1, 5, 9, 13, 17, 21 **Improving Sentences** Lessons: 1, 5, 9, 13, 17, 21 **Improving Paragraphs** Lessons: 3, 7, 11, 15, 19 **Writing** Lessons: 1, 3, 5, 7, 9, 11, 13, 15, 17, 19, 21

Vocabulary Acquisition and Use

L.9-10.4	Determine or clarify the meaning of unknown and multiple-meaning words and phrases based on grades 9–10 reading and content, choosing flexibly from a range of strategies.	**Critical Reading** Lessons: 1-21
L.9-10.4a	Use context (e.g., the overall meaning of a sentence, paragraph, or text; a word's position or function in a sentence) as a clue to the meaning of a word or phrase.	**Word in Context** Lessons: 1-21 **Inference** Lessons: 1-21 **Critical Reading** Lessons: 1-21
L.9-10.4b	Identify and correctly use patterns of word changes that indicate different meanings or parts of speech (e.g., analyze, analysis, analytical; advocate, advocacy).	**Roots, Prefixes, and Suffixes** Lessons: 1-21
L.9-10.4d	Verify the preliminary determination of the meaning of a word or phrase (e.g., by checking the inferred meaning in context or in a dictionary).	**Inference** Lessons: 1-21
L.9-10.5	Demonstrate understanding of figurative language, word relationships, and nuances in word meanings.	**Related Words, Deeper Meaning** Lessons: 1-3, 4-6, 7-9, 10-12, 13-15, 16-18, 19-21
L.9-10.5b	Analyze nuances in the meaning of words with similar denotations.	**Critical Reading** Lessons: 2, 4, 6, 8, 10, 12, 14, 16, 18, 20
L.9-10.6	Acquire and use accurately general academic and domain-specific words and phrases, sufficient for reading, writing, speaking, and listening at the college and career readiness level; demonstrate independence in gathering vocabulary knowledge when considering a word or phrase important to comprehension or expression.	**Level Nine** Lessons: 1-21

History/Social Studies

Key Ideas and Details

RH.9-10.1.	Cite specific textual evidence to support analysis of primary and secondary sources, attending to such features as the date and origin of the information.	**Critical Reading** Lessons: 2, 4, 6, 8, 10, 12, 14, 16, 18, 20

Craft and Structure

RH.9-10.4	Determine the meaning of words and phrases as they are used in a text, including vocabulary describing political, social, or economic aspects of history/social science.	**Critical Reading** Lessons: 2, 4, 6, 8, 10, 12, 14, 16, 18, 20
RH.9-10.6	Compare the point of view of two or more authors for how they treat the same or similar topics, including which details they include and emphasize in their respective accounts.	**Critical Reading** Lessons: 4, 8, 12, 16, 20

Integration of Knowledge and Ideas

RH.9-10.9	Compare and contrast treatments of the same topic in several primary and secondary sources.	**Critical Reading** Lessons: 4, 8, 12, 16, 20